From MARGARET MEAD's *introduction to*

MEN: THE VARIETY AND MEANING OF THEIR SEXUAL EXPERIENCE

"Modern civilized man is seen as bedeviled by sex, with never the right amount at the right time with the right person, distracted by little understood desires during boyhood, retiring into apathy or unsuccessful infidelity in middle age. Sex, we are told, is fine in the right place; only, as it is, it is almost always in the wrong place. . . . In the United States we have come to call the details of mating behavior 'the facts of life,' and by so doing have tended to ignore how much broader and deeper the whole question of human sex behavior is, permeating the whole of life from birth to death. . . . In this very confusion and contradiction lies the core of man's dilemma: how to make something more out of his sexual nature than 'just sex,' without making so much more that somehow his capacity for primary sex enjoyment gets lost in the process. . . ."

You will wish to read the companion volume, edited by A. M. Krich with an Introduction by Margaret Mead.

WOMEN: THE VARIETY AND MEANING OF THEIR SEXUAL EXPERIENCE

ARON KRICH, ED.D., who compiled this unique collection, is a psychologist who practices psychotherapy and marriage counseling in New York City. He is the editor of *The ~~~~~~ Women; The Hom~~~~~~~~~~~~~~~~* Mudd, *Man and W~~~~~~~~~~ Attitudes, Sexual ~~~~~~~~ ~~~~~~ seling.*

Edited by A. M. KRICH

Introduction by MARGARET MEAD

Men

The Variety and Meaning of

Their Sexual Experience

A LAUREL EDITION

Editor's Preface

SEX is the most intimate human activity. Its consequences are the most public. For the sexual impulse forces us to come out of ourselves, and by the love it commands, determines our view of ourselves, our relations with other people, and, ultimately, all the institutions of society. This dynamic influence at every turn of life is what we wanted to show through the twenty-six contributions that make up the companion volumes of *Men* and *Women*.

Essentially, a book of this kind is the achievement of its contributors. We are indebted to them, the pioneers as well as the contemporary investigators, for humanizing the study of sex. Their researches break with the unhealthy tradition of "hush and pretend" that had stamped sex as something simultaneously sacred and obscene. The wide dissemination of their perceptions and insights through the medium of popular-priced books is significant. It is proof of how far we have come since the days when Havelock Ellis pleaded that withholding the best sex instruction is like refusing to supply pure water because there are puddles in the street to drink from.

In these pages you will find thoughtful and thorough consideration of the major aspects of sex in relation to self, society, and the species. Though the material is divided into two volumes according to sex counterparts, the book you hold in your hand is complete in itself. An examination of the life of the loved must be an examination of the life of the lover. The act of sex is a union. The separate volumes dramatize this coming together.

By turning to the corresponding chapter in the companion volume the reader may understand what differences the same experience holds for the man and for the woman. For example, in *Women* a hundred husbands tell us what they feel is wrong with their marriage; the verdict of their wives is given in *Men*. In *Women,* we meet "the sowers of wild oats," a group of college girls who took sex where they found it. In *Men,* we meet the "hot-bloods," the boys they found it with. Potency and receptivity, frigidity and impotence, motherhood and fatherhood, are similarly paired. If our editorial plan has been at all successful, the two books should fulfill each other as male and female do in life.

The inspiration to present the material in this way came from Margaret Mead. Indeed, what is uncommon about this book—the many kinds of questions it raises and answers with a minimum of the arrogant assumptions and convenient fabrications sometimes found in books about sex—must be credited to the stimulating collaboration of this remarkable scientist and woman. In building both books, Dr. Mead was the architect. The editor carried the bricks. We hope we have built well.

—*A. M. Krich*

Table of Contents

(continued on next page)

INTRODUCTION

by Margaret Mead

Pᴇᴏᴘʟᴇ sᴏᴍᴇᴛɪᴍᴇs sᴘᴇᴀᴋ of "The Sex Problem" in very much the same tone of voice as they speak of "The Labor Problem," as if it were a new kind of nuisance that had arisen along with modern factories or airplanes. Behind the tone of their voices there is the assumption that long ago—in great-grandfather's day, or in the Middle Ages, or possibly in the Old Stone Age—there were no sex problems, and each man grew up and mated in the ways that the rest of his society approved of—and that was that. Conversely, modern civilized man is seen as bedeviled by sex, with never the right amount at the right time with the right person, distracted by little understood desires during boyhood, trapped into early marriage in young manhood, retiring into apathy or unsuccessful infidelity in middle age. Sex, we are told, is fine in the right place; only, as it is, it is almost always in the wrong place. And by sex, these carping critics mean specific acts of sex—for in the United States we have come to call the details of mating behavior "the facts of life" and by so doing have tended to ignore how much broader and deeper the whole question of human sex behavior is, permeating the whole of life from birth to death, concerned in the design of dwelling houses, the tax rate for schools, the policies of armies, the practices of

churches. Sex is, in fact, taken in this broader
sense, the very stuff of life, the biological device
through which, in all higher living forms, offspring may be diversified from their parents and
the species varied constructively, the biological
device through which parents are kept together
so that offspring can be given enough time to
develop into complicated creatures.

If we say that men work and fight, plow the
fields and harvest grain, in fulfillment of their
sexual role in the world, and play and swim and
ski and climb mountains, dance and sing and
drive cars, also in fulfillment of their sexual role,
learning to be gay, sure-footed, happy lovers if
they are to win and to keep satisfactory lifelong
companions, then sex can be seen as involving
the whole of life, preparatory for and following
naturally upon the particular acts which we cus-
tomarily think of as sexual. Even in the activities
in which men turn from women and children,
or even turn from each other, becoming sailors
or monks or hermits, the style of their segrega-
tion or asceticism is given by the circumstance
that all men have been born into a world organized around sex; if no men married, bachelor-
hood and celibacy would have little meaning.

But although one can make a quite con-
vincing case for this permeation of life by man's
sexuality—discussing birth and marriage and parenthood, architecture and painting, mountain
climbing and airplane flying, all as expressions
in one way or another of man's basic role—one
immediately encounters two forms of opposition
from opposite camps. One group of critics says

that one is—like Freud—reducing everything to just sex, and by sex they mean what Kinsey means by sex behavior—activity leading specifically to a release of physical tension. This reduction is unjustified, they claim; love, marriage, religion are much more than this—as they surely are.

The other set of critics claims that one is dodging the question, talking about matters that are social, political, and philosophical, when the *basic* question—as an eighteen-year-old recently phrased it to me in a large open forum in a religious building—is simply "Do you or don't you?" His was also a reducing question, for he was saying in effect: "I want to know under what conditions, with whom, I may engage in sex activity, and I am totally uninterested in any other question." His was the question of the young man who has not yet been in love, for whom, at least while his love is blooming, such a question will fall into the perspective provided by tender responsibility and a desire to secure the girl forever.

The first objection, on the other hand, comes from the man who has either never known love, or known it so long ago that he has forgotten what it was like, who certainly never succeeded in reaching satisfactory fusing of his individual aspirations and a primary sex experience, and who now cannot bear to have his achievements as husband, father, banker, or preacher, reduced to what, in his memory, are a set of unsatisfactory, unintegrated experiences.

So from those who have not yet integrated

the eager specificity of their bodies into an inter-personal pattern and likewise from those who have given up the attempt, there comes, in effect, the same statement: "What you call sex is nothing but a physical act." The members of one group say, "Stop mentioning it among higher things," and the others say, "Stop avoiding the real issue by talking about higher things."

In this very confusion and contradiction—in the phrases "just sex," "nothing but sex," whether couched in twentieth-century language or not —lies the core of man's dilemma: how to make something more out of his sexual nature than "just sex," without making so much more that—having built himself a fine superstructure of chivalry, poetry, and public works—somehow his capacity for primary sex enjoyment gets lost in the process, and from his heights of civilization he finds that he must look down on activities that have somehow failed to be included in the meanings he tried to give them.

This has been man's problem from the simplest civilizations of which we have record. Every human society, from the days when men wandered without clothes, carrying fire sticks in their hands to keep themselves warm, has had to deal with the possibility that human beings, if their impulses were undisciplined, were just as capable of falling in love with members of their own families as with other people—possibly more so, as close association, tender care, eating together all occurred within the family group. And in every human society such relationships are forbidden—the incest taboo is universal. The family is protected from conflicts between father and son, between brothers over a sister, from rivalry between mother and daughter. Each generation has to go out and find new mates, and a wider society is guaranteed. Tension, delay, difficulty, the complications of inhibiting one's possible affection for those close to oneself, the complication of courting the daughters and sisters of other men, enter in. There is delay, perhaps years of delay—as, for example, for a young man among the Indians of the North American Plains, where courtship might involve years of hunting cautiously with the brother of the beloved before one even had a chance to speak to her. And with such delay, there were always twin possibilities: marriage when it came might seem worth all the waiting, so that every whisper of the wife who had been so hard to attain was ineffably exciting, or the habit of waiting might have hardened into a physical indifference underlying a passionate romanticism. Among one of these Indian groups, a marriage based on many years of shy courtship was said to crack if the first baby died, the long waiting and the fury of grief combining in a passion of mutual accusation.

At some periods in history, or for the members of some classes, the solution has been to divide the life cycle into two parts, freedom to make love lightly and without undue commitment during late adolescence, and a demand that love be combined with responsibility and fatherhood after marriage. Or, instead of dividing life in half, women might be divided up, "bad women"

for "just sex" and "good women" who were
suitable wives and mothers, but with whom sex
activity was inhibited and unrewarding. Or sex
behavior might be divided up by place—men
would be discreet and orderly in their own communities, never glancing at another man's sweet-
heart or wife, and promiscuous and irresponsible
in other towns, where they went as travelers, as
soldiers or sailors ashore.

In every society, in every period of history,
and in complicated societies like ours, among
different classes of people—farmers as compared
with urban workers—people have tried to establish some balance between sex that dominated
all the richer complications of love and friendship, responsibility and religion and parenthood
on the one hand, and such a heavy emphasis on
all these considerations that simple bodily joy
gets lost in the process, on the other. There have
always been a host of difficulties to overcome.
For while society tends to set up ways of behav-
ing to which everyone is expected to conform,
human beings differ enormously, and perhaps in
no respect as much as in their capacity for sex
activity. The rhythm of desire normal for one
man might mean severe abstinence for a second
and seem to be a wild and debilitating debauch
to a third. Yet where sex activities are shrouded
with a veil of reticence or prudery, these differences are not known, even between friends or
brothers, and women have no idea what to expect. Girls who have absorbed one standard of
expectation may be affronted hopelessly by some
slight manifestation of physical ardor; others,

who have picked up some other expectation, may be repelled by the same behavior because they experience it as showing coldness and lack of feeling. Most people make many jokes about the wedding night and it is worth noting that they make these jokes both in societies in which there is great sexual freedom for men and in those in which there is not; the point to the wedding-night joke is the conflict between a set schedule introduced by social convention and the varying rhythms and readinesses of individual men. For some men it is enough to set the scene for desire to arise, for others nothing is less attractive than scene-setting by someone else. Yet in this respect and in many others, society—in the persons of parents, friends, wives, and sweethearts—tends to treat all men alike. When the convention lays stress on their too great potentiality for "just sex" under all and any circumstances, men are expected to "behave like beasts," girls are properly warned against them, and in a world which prickles with prohibitions and chaperons, feminine screams and fainting fits, those men whose natural or learned sex behavior approximated most closely to that of "beasts" were at home, while other men simply withdrew into themselves and raised flowers.

Complex civilizations add a third factor of risk. In every society, in every class in a complex society, there are traditional ways by which small boys and girls are expected to learn about sex behavior, all the way from how to feel about their own bodies and those of the opposite sex, to how husbands and wives and fathers and mothers should behave. Here, too, as children, in the family, they learn when to be romantic and when practical, when looks count more than ability, at what point a boy had better begin to ask whether a girl is likely to inherit land, or knows how to cook, or darn socks. Children who share one room with their parents learn very early how married people might be expected to behave, while children who are tucked away in a far-off nursery with an unmarried nurse have to learn a great many things later in life. The sex behavior of these isolated ones is more likely to depend on the way a woman is dressed; they often find it impossible to court anyone but a "lady," or, on the other hand, ever to have any physical response at all to anyone who looks like a "lady."

Each of these systems of bringing up children to play a full sexual role in their particular society is very elaborate, each part depending upon a large number of things, such as both parents' being alive; if the grandmothers were part of the usual plan—expected, for example, to sleep with the second child when mother had a new baby—then there had to be a grandmother alive and present. If the plan called for nurses, nurses were needed. Doors, curtains, lamps, all had to be in the usual places so that the children saw and heard what they were expected to see and hear, and not different things. When such systems work, they have great advantages. Children grow up without realizing what they are learning, "gentlemen" learn to feel that only girls reared as "ladies" are worthy of love, farmers learn to marry husky girls who have strength left for love-making even after helping with the haying.

But even in the simplest human societies these things never worked out perfectly; parents died and children were reared by grandparents too old to serve as visible models of behavior or who could only teach the children part of the pattern. A man's wife might be so ailing that the father cared for the children in some way that men were not expected to care for children, thus damaging the expected development of son or daughter. The occasional insane person, whom we know today as the sex criminal, attacked or at least frightened some children. More distant relatives, especially in unusual situations, broke the incest taboos; men seduced their wives' younger sisters, or women their husbands' younger brothers. Servant girls seduced adolescent boys where such behavior brought parental wrath and indignation, as well as in the societies where servant girls were expected to play this role. The whole educational system, by which boys and girls were expected to learn something far more complex and delicately balanced than the three R's, has always been only partially successful, has never provided for all the differences between individual children, between individual families, for the disorganization in the patterns arising from early death or remarriage, still less for immigration, famine, hurricane, or war.

So, whatever arrangements exist in a society to insure that growing children will learn to play the appropriate roles, to feel desire when desire

is appropriate, to be shy, modest, repelled, or
indifferent when it is not—these arrangements
have always been far from perfect. The imperfec-
tions show up in figures on juvenile delinquency,
crime, alcoholism, and various kinds of mental
breakdown. Failure to give children the proper
preparation for their full sexual functioning in
life is of course not the sole cause of these social
breakdowns—there are many others, such as in-
equalities of economic opportunity, economic
disasters, breakdown in the system of police and
government, etc. But many men go into the
antisocial positions of the criminal, the alcoholic,
the tramp, simply because they never had the
chance to learn how to have a happy, full life as
a lover, a friend, a husband, a father, a father-in-
law, and a grandfather—all roles which actively
involve sexuality. As lovers they may perhaps
ask but never give pleasure; as friends of their
own sex they may perhaps involve too much of
the physical desire which this society expects to
have specialized for women alone; as husbands
they may know of no way of varying the monotony of monogamous marriage, or they may wish
to vary it beyond the limits of their wives' tolerance and understanding. In a thousand ways
we can find discrepancies between natural endowment and sexual vigor, between the ways in
which a man or a boy of a given age or class is
expected to behave, and the way in which, in
fact, he actually does behave.

This situation is as old as history; social order
has been purchased by all sorts of human sacrifices, not only the sacrifice of a hundred captives

on the altars of pagan gods, or the sacrifice of millions of men in warfare, but by subtler sacrifices of zest and joy, of human capacities for love and tenderness, and by those mutilations of the human spirit that produce the joyless prostitute and the sex criminal. The articles in this book, chosen from a wide range of authors, written over the last fifty years, represent a new approach to the question of how men and women, as individuals and as members of society, can use their intelligence and the new methods of science to reduce the number of misfits, the number of joyless marriages, the number of the impotent, the obsessed, the driven, the withdrawn, and the loveless in any generation.

Substantially, the pioneers in sex research who are represented in this volume did a number of things that it took courage and imagination to do. First, they broke the taboo on what could and could not be talked about and written about. They said: Let us find out what really goes on in human lives, the dreams and fantasies as well as the actual overt behavior, what really happens behind the agonized reticence of the spinster or the widow, to what depths of guilt and fear adolescents who do not understand what is happening to them can be driven. So they began to investigate, Havelock Ellis as a student of sex behavior, Freud as a physician who had found that back of many of the complaints that his patients brought him lay disorders in sexual behavior, in the ability to make love, to accept the responsibilities of marriage, to be faithful or tender, and that these disorders could be traced to situations in early childhood, reactivated and reinforced by later life events. They tore the veil that had been one of the ways in which society had maintained a balance between individual differences and rigid social roles, between expected life experience and real experience.

To this, as was to be predicted, the custodians of the current status of social attitudes about sex responded with vigorous denunciations. It took a quarter of a century to reach the next stage, when sex research could be done by people without vigor and crusading zeal for a new approach to human behavior. But slowly the world grew accustomed to the new ideas; Freud's theories became the basis of a recognized form of therapy, especially for those whose deepest sexual adjustments had been disturbed. Havelock Ellis's belief that ignorance was one of the principal causes of maladjustment in individuals and of cruelty in society became more widely accepted. Foundations gave money for research in sex behavior, for studies like Hamilton's and later for Kinsey's ambitious survey of what specific acts men said they engaged in and had engaged in during their entire lives.

Today, the climate of opinion is a very different one from that in which Freud's early findings were denounced, and Havelock Ellis—passionate apostle of the sacredness and beauty of lifelong marriage that gives full play to both passion and fidelity—was read as pornographic literature by salacious-minded boys, victims of the prudery in which they had been reared, and unprepared for the confusions of a transition period. We have lived through the revolution in manners that followed World War I, when women bobbed their hair and shortened their skirts, and mothers, envying their daughters a freedom they themselves had never had, set out to recapture the delights of adolescence. We have lived through the Depression, with its postponed marriages and postponed parenthood, its shift in intellectual interest from the sexual and personal problems of the individual to the economic problems of the nation. We have lived through World War II, with the increasing demand for early marriage and the postwar demand for early and frequent parenthood. As the hopes of a completely peaceful world have dwindled, a counterpoint has grown up in which young people oppose their demands for personal happiness to the uncertainties of the Atomic Age, and insist on help in their early marriages and early parenthood, as they did in wartime.

We may be said to have reached, socially, a new kind of adjustment, better fitted to the present position of women, and to an age in which salaries and pension plans are replacing property as a protection for the individual and the family, and the certainty of some military service is replacing the periodic shock of unexpected mobilization. With real coeducation, great freedom of dress, and economic freedom for women before marriage, the sorts of controls —shyness, fear, and chaperonage—that regulated premarital behavior have melted away. Young people can face more frankly, and more articulately, the problems of full sex adjustment that confront them. But if they are to do so, then knowledge is needed, and needed more than it has ever been.

As the society permits so much freedom of choice and choice within a single class, premarital and extramarital relationships within one's own class are becoming the expected form of deviations from strict monogamy, and the prostitute and the kept woman are alike dwindling in importance. But this means that individual pairs of young people must be well informed about the whole range of possibilities if they are to make intelligent choices, as they can no longer rely on parents, neighbors, or police to curb their impulses and narrow their solutions down. Thus knowledge about sex—sex in its widest sense as it involves the whole of the personality, and the whole of the individual's life choices, and sex in its narrowest sense, as the possibilities in the arts of love-making—becomes imperatively important.

There are inevitably those who will continue to question whether it is wise to tell people, especially people younger than they, so much. There will be others who feel that it is equally unwise to tell much older people so much, and that the adolescents of the past had a better time in the days when their parents did not know what to suspect them of. There are those who feel that the bloom of modesty, expressed in an inability to name important parts of the body, gave great charm to women—at least to the woman one married—which is lost in the frankness of the present day. Quite expectably, many young people resent having some of the protections of ignorance torn from them in a country in which we are short on individual ethical standards and long on conforming to one's own age group. A generation of young men who restricted their sex activities, not from conviction but because they believed others did, have been left defenseless by the Kinsey report. A generation of earnest elders who were able to tolerate more straight talk about sex than they had thought they could, because it was regarded as part of the whole of life, found themselves newly repelled by the stark definitions of the Kinsey report, which treated man as a somewhat dull animal, responding to no pattern except that of socio-economic class, in search of temporary relief of tension and relatively indifferent to what sort of object was utilized.

Other critics of our present-day customs are worried by the increase in crime, especially juvenile crime, often failing to see that the new climate of opinion has hardly arrived, that as yet it only affects a very small number of teachers, judges, social workers, physicians, and a small number of adolescents who have been reared in the special kind of frankness and ease toward which we seem to be moving. So the very newest attempts at a healthy nursery-school life are treated as causes of delinquency that started many years ago. It seems rather that we should recognize the prophetic foresight of men like Freud and Havelock Ellis, who realized onto what perilous shoals of personal disorganization the people of the Western world were drifting, and set up new beacons that are just beginning to guide us, but not before many people's lives have been wrecked.

Young men in the mid 1950's are asking the same question that young men in America have always asked: how to achieve monogamous, life-long happy marriages, and these without any subsidiary support from prostitution or liaisons. Faced with many great opportunities for adolescent experiment, they are beginning to work out their own codes of adolescent ethics, which culminate in the increased insistence on the right to marry early and to have their children early. As the older sanctions that used to keep a marriage going crumble away—indissoluble marriage, religious denunciation, loss of status and job— new reasons for staying married are developing, the most important of which seems to be the increasing enjoyment that young fathers take in their children. For the old shared things—house, farm, ancestrally defined position, respectability —young people who have married since World War II are substituting a common enjoyment of life in the present and in the details of the rearing of several children.

This selection contains thirteen articles by different writers from different periods. It is designed neither as prescription nor prophecy, but as a way of opening the eyes of the reader to the significance of parts of life that he or she may have missed, to the intricate complexity of man's sexual development and to its implications for human fulfillment.

1.

The Sexual Life of Man

by Sigmund Freud

Through its influence on all disciplines that deal with individual and social behavior, the work of Sigmund Freud has molded modern attitudes in ways too manifold to measure. Nowhere has this impact been greater than on the study of sex. Extensive discussion of Freudian concepts will be found in the chapters listed below. Here, the heart of Freud's theories on the special role played by infantile sexuality in the development of the adult personality is presented in a popular lecture, one of a series of twenty-eight originally delivered at the University of Vienna during the years 1915-1917. Reprinted from *A General Introduction to Psychoanalysis* by Sigmund Freud, copyright, 1935, by Edward L. Bernays, copyright, 1948, by Susie Hoch, by permission of Liveright Publishing Corporation and George Allen & Unwin Ltd.

See also Chapters 1, 2, 8, 10, 11 in *Women:* "The Sexual Impulse and the Art of Love," "Prepuberty in Woman," "The Unmarried," "Changing Concepts of Homosexuality," "The Abnormality of Prostitution."

ONE WOULD CERTAINLY THINK that there could be no doubt about what is to be understood by the term "sexual." First and foremost, of course, it means the "improper," that which must not be mentioned. I have been told a story about some pupils of a famous psychiatrist, who once endeavored to convince their master that the symptoms of an hysteric are frequently representations of sexual things. With this object, they took him to the bedside of an hysterical woman whose attacks were unmistakable imitations of childbirth. He objected, how-

ever: "Well, there is nothing sexual about childbirth."
To be sure, childbirth is not necessarily always improper.

I perceive that you don't approve of my joking about
such serious matters. It is not altogether a joke, however.
Seriously, it is not so easy to define what the term sexual
includes. Everything connected with the difference between the two sexes is perhaps the only way of hitting
the mark; but you will find that too general and indefi-
nite. If you take the sexual act itself as the central point,
you will perhaps declare sexual to mean everything
which is concerned with obtaining pleasurable gratification from the body (and particularly the sexual organs)
of the opposite sex; in the narrowest sense, everything
which is directed to the union of the genital organs and
the performance of the sexual act. In doing so, however,
you come very near to reckoning the sexual and the improper as identical, and childbirth would really have
nothing to do with sex. If then you make the function
of reproduction the kernel of sexuality you run the risk
of excluding from it a whole host of things like masturbation, or even kissing, which are not directed towards
reproduction, but which are nevertheless undoubtedly
sexual. However, we have already found that attempts
at definition always lead to difficulties; let us give up
trying to do any better in this particular case. We may
suspect that in the development of the concept "sexual"
something has happened which has resulted in what H.
Silberer has aptly called a "covering error." On the
whole, indeed, we know pretty well what is meant by
sexual.

In the popular view, which is sufficient for all practical
purposes in ordinary life, sexual is something which com-
bines references to the difference between the sexes, to
pleasurable excitement and gratification, to the reproduc-

tive function, and to the idea of impropriety and the necessity for concealment. But this is no longer sufficient for science. For painstaking researches (only possible, of course, in a spirit of self-command maintained by self-sacrifice) have revealed that classes of human beings exist whose sexual life deviates from the usual one in the most striking manner. One group among these "perverts" has, as it were, expunged the difference between the sexes from its scheme of life. In these people, only the same sex as their own can rouse sexual desire; the other sex (especially the genital organ of the other sex) has absolutely no sexual attraction for them, can even in extreme cases be an object of abhorrence to them. They have thus of course foregone all participation in the process of reproduction. Such persons are called homosexuals or inverts. Often, though not always, they are men and women who otherwise have reached an irreproachable high standard of mental growth and development, intellectually and ethically, and are only afflicted with this one fateful peculiarity. Through the mouths of their scientific spokesmen they lay claim to be a special variety of the human race, a "third sex," as they call it, standing with equal rights alongside the other two. We may perhaps have an opportunity of critically examining these claims. They are not, of course, as they would gladly maintain, the "elect" of mankind; they contain in their ranks at least as many inferior and worthless individuals as are to be found among those differently constituted sexually.

These perverts do at least seek to achieve very much the same ends with the objects of their desires as normal people do with theirs. But after them comes a long series of abnormal types, in whom the sexual activities become increasingly further removed from anything which ap-

pears attractive to a reasonable being. In their manifold
variety and their strangeness these types may be compared to the grotesque monstrosities painted by P.
Breughel to represent the temptation of St. Anthony, or
to the long procession of effete gods and worshippers
which G. Flaubert shows us passing before his pious
penitent, and to nothing else. The chaotic assembly calls
out for classification if it is not to bewilder us completely. We divide them into those in whom the *sexual object*
has been altered, as with the homosexuals, and those in
whom, first and foremost, the *sexual aim* has been altered. In the first group belong those who have dispensed
with the mutual union of the genital organs and who
have substituted for the genitals, in one of the partners
in the act, another organ or part of the body (mouth or
anus, in place of the vagina) making light of both the
anatomical difficulties and the suppression of disgust involved. There follow others who, it is true, still retain
the genital organs as object; not, however, by virtue of
their sexual function, but on account of other functions
in which they take part anatomically or by reason of
their proximity. These people demonstrate that the excretory functions, which in the course of the child's upbringing are relegated to a limbo as indecent, remain
capable of attracting the entire sexual interest. There
are others who have given up altogether the genital
organs as object; and, instead, have exalted some other
part of the body to serve as the object of desire, a woman's breast, foot, or plait of hair. There are others yet to
whom even a part of the body is meaningless, while a
particle of clothing, a shoe or a piece of underclothing,
will gratify all their desires; these are the fetishists.
Farther on in the scale come those who indeed demand
the object as a whole: but whose requirements in regard

to it take specific forms, of an extraordinary or horrible nature—even to the point of seeking it as a defenseless corpse and, urged on by their criminal obsessions, of making it one in order so to enjoy it. But enough of these horrors!

Foremost in the second group are those perverts whose sexual desires aim at the performance of an act which normally is but an introductory or preparatory one. They are those who seek gratification in looking and touching, or in watching the other person's most intimate doings; or those who expose parts of their own bodies which should be concealed, in the vague expectation of being rewarded by a similar action on the part of the other. Then come the incomprehensible sadists, in whom all affectionate feeling strains toward the one goal of causing their object pain and torture, ranging in degree from mere indications of a tendency to humiliate the other up to the infliction of severe bodily injuries. Then, as though complementary to these, come the masochists, whose only longing is to suffer, in real or in symbolic form, humiliations and tortures at the hands of the loved object. There are others yet, in whom several abnormal characteristics of this kind are combined and interwoven with one another. Finally, we learn that the persons belonging to each of these groups may be divided again: into those who seek their particular form of sexual satisfaction in reality and those who are satisfied merely to imagine it in their own minds, needing no real object at all but being able to substitute for it a creation of fantasy.

There is not the slightest possible doubt that these mad, extraordinary and horrible things do actually constitute the sexual activities of these people. Not merely do they themselves so regard them, recognizing their substitutive character; but we also have to acknowledge that they play the same part in their lives as normal sexual satisfaction plays in ours, exacting the same, often excessive, sacrifices. It is possible to trace out, both broadly and in great detail, where these abnormalities merge into the normal and where they diverge from it. Nor will it escape you that that quality of impropriety which adheres inevitably to a sexual activity is not absent from these forms of it: in most of them it is intensified to the point of odium.

Well, now, what attitude are we to take up to these unusual forms of sexual satisfaction? Indignation and expressions of our personal disgust, together with assurances that we do not share these appetites, will obviously not carry us very far. That is not the point at issue. After all, this is a field of phenomena like any other; attempts to turn away and flee from it, on the pretext that these are but rarities and curiosities, could easily be rebutted. On the contrary, the phenomena are common enough and widely distributed. But if it is objected that our views on the sexual life of mankind require no revision on this account, since these things are one and all aberrations and divagations of the sexual instinct, a serious reply will be necessary. If we do not understand these morbid forms of sexuality and cannot relate them to what is normal in sexual life, then neither can we understand normal sexuality. It remains, in short, our undeniable duty to account satisfactorily in theory for the existence of all the perversions described and to explain their relation to normal sexuality, so-called.

In this task we can be helped by a point of view, and by two new evidential observations. The first we owe to Ivan Bloch; according to him, the view that all the perversions are "signs of degeneration" is incorrect, because of the evidence existing that such aberrations from the sexual aim, such erratic relationships to the sexual object, have been manifested since the beginning of time through every age of which we have knowledge, in every race from the most primitive to the most highly civilized, and at times have succeeded in attaining to toleration and general prevalence. The two evidential observations have been made in the course of psychoanalytic investigations of neurotic patients; they must undoubtedly influence our conception of sexual perversions in a decisive manner.

We have said that neurotic symptoms are substitutes for sexual satisfactions and I have already indicated that many difficulties will be met with in proving this statement from the analysis of symptoms. It is, indeed, only accurate if the "perverse" sexual needs, so-called, are included under the sexual satisfactions; for an interpretation of the symptoms on this basis is forced upon us with astonishing frequency. The claim made by homosexuals or inverts, that they constitute a select class of mankind, falls at once to the ground when we discover that in every single neurotic evidence of homosexual tendencies is forthcoming and that a large proportion of the symptoms are expressions of this latent inversion. Those who openly call themselves homosexuals are merely those in whom the inversion is conscious and manifest; their number is negligible compared with those in whom it is latent. We are bound, in fact, to regard the choice of an object of the same sex as a regular type of offshoot of the capacity to love, and are learning every day more and more to recognize it as especially important. The differences between manifest homosexuality and the normal attitude are certainly not thereby abrogated; they have their practical importance, which remains, but theoretically their value is very considerably diminished. In fact, we have even come to the conclusion that one particular mental disorder, paranoia, no longer to be reckoned among the transference neuroses, invariably arises from an attempt to subdue unduly powerful homosexual tendencies. Perhaps you will remember that one of our patients, in her obsessive act, played the part of a man—of her own husband, that is, whom she had left; such symptoms, representing the impersonation of a man, are very commonly produced by neurotic women. If this is not actually attributable to homosexuality, it is certainly very closely connected with its origins.

As you probably know, the neurosis of hysteria can create its symptoms in all systems of the body (circulatory, respiratory, etc.) and may thus disturb all the functions. Analysis shows that all those impulses, described as perverse, which aim at replacing the genital organ by another come to expression in these symptoms. These organs thus behave as substitutes for the genital organs: it is precisely from the study of hysterical symptoms that we have arrived at the view that, besides their functional role, a sexual—*erotogenic*—significance must be ascribed to the bodily organs; and that the needs of the former will be interfered with if the demands of the latter upon them are too great. Countless sensations and innervations, which we meet as hysterical symptoms, in organs apparently not concerned with sexuality, are thus discovered to be essentially fulfillments of perverse sexual desires, by the other organs having usurped the function of the genitalia. In this way also the very great extent to which the organs of nutrition and of excretion, in particular, may serve in yielding sexual excitement is brought home to us. It is indeed the same thing as is manifested in the perversions; except that in the latter

it is unmistakable and recognizable without any difficulty, whereas in hysteria we have to make the detour of
interpreting the symptom, and then do not impute the
perverse sexual impulse in question to the person's consciousness, but account it to the unconscious part of his
personality.

Of the many types of symptom characteristic of the obsessional neurosis the most important are found to be
brought about by the undue strength of one group of
sexual tendencies with a perverted aim, i.e. the sadistic
group. These symptoms, in accordance with the structure
of the obsessional neurosis, serve mainly as a defense
against these wishes or else they express the conflict between satisfaction and rejection. Satisfaction does not
find short shrift, however; it knows how to get its own
way by a roundabout route in the patient's behavior, by
preference turning against him in self-inflicted torment.
Other forms of this neurosis are seen in excessive "worry"
and brooding; these are the expressions of an exaggerated
sexualization of acts which are normally only preparatory to sexual satisfaction: the desire to see, to touch
and to investigate. In this lies the explanation of the
very great importance dread of contact and obsessive
washing attains to in this disease. An unsuspectedly
large proportion of obsessive actions are found to be
disguised repetitions and modifications of masturbation,
admittedly the only uniform act which accompanies all
the varied flights of sexual fantasy.

It would not be difficult to show you the connections
between perversion and neurosis in a much more detailed manner, but I believe that I have said enough for
our purposes. We must beware, however, of overesti-
mating the frequency and intensity of the perverse tendencies in mankind, after these revelations of their im-

portance in the interpretation of symptoms. You have heard that frustration of normal sexual satisfactions may lead to the development of neurosis. In consequence of this frustration in reality the need is forced into the abnormal paths of sexual excitation. Later you will be able to understand how this happens. You will at any rate understand that a "collateral" damming-up of this kind must swell the force of the perverse impulses, so that they become more powerful than they would have been had no hindrance to normal sexual satisfaction been present in reality. Incidentally, a similar factor may be recognized also in the manifest perversions. In many cases they are provoked or activated by the unduly great difficulties in the way of normal satisfaction of the sexual instinct which are produced either by temporary conditions or by permanent social institutions. In other cases, certainly, perverse tendencies are quite independent of such conditions; they are, as it were, the natural kind of sexual life for the individual concerned.

Perhaps you are momentarily under the impression that all this tends to confuse rather than to explain the relations between normal and perverted sexuality. But keep in mind this consideration. If it is correct that real obstacles to sexual satisfaction or frustration in regard to it bring to the surface perverse tendencies in people who would otherwise have shown none, we must conclude that something in these people is ready to embrace the perversions; or, if you prefer it, the tendencies must have been present in them in a latent form. Thus we come to the second of the new evidential observations of which I spoke. Psychoanalytic investigation has found it necessary also to concern itself with the sexual life of children, for the reason that in the analysis of symptoms the forthcoming reminiscences and associations invariably lead back to the earliest years of childhood. That which we discovered in this way has since been corroborated point by point by the direct observation of children. In this way it has been found that all the perverse tendencies have their roots in childhood, that children are disposed toward them all and practice them all to a degree conforming with their immaturity; in short, *perverted sexuality* is nothing else but infantile sexuality, magnified and separated into its component parts.

Now you will see the perversions in an altogether different light and no longer ignore their connection with the sexual life of mankind; but what distressing emotions these astonishing and grotesque revelations will provoke in you! At first you will certainly be tempted to deny everything—the fact that there is anything in children which can be termed sexual life, the accuracy of our observations, and the justification of our claim to see in the behavior of children any connection with that which in later years is condemned as perverted. Permit me first to explain to you the motives of your antagonism and then to put before you a summary of our observations. That children should have no sexual life—sexual excitement, needs, and gratification of a sort—but that they suddenly acquire these things in the years between twelve and fourteen would be, apart from any observations at all, biologically just as improbable, indeed, nonsensical, as to suppose that they are born without genital organs which first begin to sprout at the age of puberty. What does actually awake in them at this period is the reproductive function, which then makes use for its own purposes of material lying to hand in body and mind. You are making the mistake of confounding sexuality and reproduction with each other and thus you obstruct your own way to the comprehension of sexuality, the perversions, and the neuroses. This mistake, moreover, has a meaning in it. Strange to say, its origin lies in the fact that you yourselves have all been children and as children were subject to the influences of education. For it is indeed one of the most important social tasks of education to restrain, confine, and subject to an individual control (itself identical with the demands of society) the sexual instinct when it breaks forth in the form of the reproductive function. In its own interests, accordingly, society would postpone the child's full development until it has attained a certain stage of intellectual maturity, since educability practically ceases with the full onset of the sexual instinct. Without this the instinct would break all bounds and the laboriously erected structure of civilization would be swept away. Nor is the task of restraining it ever an easy one; success in this direction is often poor and, sometimes, only too great. At bottom society's motive is economic; since it has not means enough to support life for its members without work on their part, it must see to it that the number of these members is restricted and their energies directed away from sexual activities on to their work—the eternal primordial struggle for existence, therefore, persisting to the present day.

Experience must have taught educators that the task of molding the sexual will of the next generation can only be carried out by beginning to impose their influence very early, and intervening in the sexual life of children before puberty, instead of waiting till the storm bursts. Consequently almost all infantile sexual activities are forbidden or made disagreeable to the child; the ideal has been to make the child's life asexual, and in course of time it has come to this that it is really believed to be asexual, and is given out as such, even at the hands

of science. In order then to avoid any contradiction with
established beliefs and aims, the sexual activity of children is overlooked—no small achievement, by the way—
while science contents itself with otherwise explaining it
away. The little child is supposed to be pure and innocent; he who says otherwise shall be condemned as a
hardened blasphemer against humanity's tenderest and
most sacred feelings.

The children alone take no part in this convention;
they assert their animal nature naively enough and demonstrate persistently that they have yet to learn their
"purity." Strange to say, those who deny sexuality in
children are the last to relax educative measures against
it; they follow up with the greatest severity every manifestation of the "childish tricks" the existence of which
they deny. Moreover, it is theoretically of great interest
that the time of life which most flagrantly contradicts
the prejudice about asexual childhood, the years of infancy up to five or six, is precisely the period which is
veiled by oblivion in most people's memories; an oblivion which can only be dispelled completely by analysis
but which even before this was sufficiently penetrable to
allow some of the dreams of childhood to be retained.

I will now tell you the most clearly recognizable of the
child's sexual activities. It will be expedient if I first
introduce you to the term *libido*. In every way analogous
to *hunger*, libido is the force by means of which the instinct, in this case the sexual instinct, as, with hunger,
the nutritional instinct, achieves expression. Other terms,
such as sexual excitation and satisfaction, require no
definition. Interpretation finds most to do in regard to
the sexual activities of the infant, as you will easily perceive; and no doubt you will find a reason for objections.
This interpretation is formed on the basis of analytic

investigation, working backwards from a given symptom. The infant's first sexual excitations appear in connection with the other functions important for life. Its chief interest, as you know, is concerned with taking nourishment; as it sinks asleep at the breast, utterly satisfied, it bears a look of perfect content which will come back again later in life after the experience of the sexual orgasm. This would not be enough to found a conclusion upon. However, we perceive that infants wish to repeat, without really getting any nourishment, the action necessary to taking nourishment; they are therefore not impelled to this by hunger. We call this action "pleasure-sucking" (German: *lutschen,* signifying the enjoyment of sucking for its own sake—as with a rubber "comforter"); and as when it does this the infant again falls asleep with a blissful expression we see that the action of sucking is sufficient in itself to give it satisfaction. Admittedly, it very soon contrives not to go to sleep without having sucked in this way. An old physician for children in Budapest, Dr. Lindner, was the first to maintain the sexual nature of this procedure. Nurses and people who look after children appear to take the same view of this pleasure-sucking, though without taking up any theoretic attitude about it. They have no doubt that its only purpose is in the pleasure derived; they account it one of the child's "naughty tricks"; and take severe measures to force it to give it up, if it will not do so of its own accord. And so we learn that an infant performs actions with no other object but that of obtaining pleasure. We believe that this pleasure is first of all experienced while nourishment is being taken, but that the infant learns rapidly to enjoy it apart from this condition. The gratification obtained can only relate to the region of the mouth and lips; we therefore call these areas of the body *erotogenic zones* and describe the pleasure derived from this sucking as a *sexual one*. To be sure, we have yet to discuss the justification for the use of this term.

If the infant could express itself it would undoubtedly acknowledge that the act of sucking at its mother's breast is far and away the most important thing in life. It would not be wrong in this, for by this act it gratifies at the same moment the two greatest needs in life. Then we learn from psychoanalysis, not without astonishment, how much of the mental significance of this act is retained throughout life. Sucking for nourishment becomes the point of departure from which the whole sexual life develops, the unattainable prototype of every later sexual satisfaction, to which in times of need fantasy often enough reverts. The desire to suck includes within it the desire for the mother's breast, which is therefore the first *object* of sexual desire; I cannot convey to you any adequate idea of the importance of this first object in determining every later object adopted, of the profound influence it exerts, through transformation and substitution, upon the most distant fields of mental life. First of all, however, as the infant takes to sucking for pleasure this object is given up and is replaced by a part of its own body; it sucks its thumb or its own tongue. For purposes of obtaining pleasure it thus makes itself independent of the concurrence of the outer world and, in addition, it extends the region of excitation to a second area of the body, thus intensifying it. The erotogenic zones are not all equally capable of yielding enjoyment; it is therefore an important experience when, as Dr. Lindner says, the infant in feeling about on its own body discovers the particularly excitable region of its genitalia, and so finds the way from pleasure-sucking to onanism.

This assessment of the nature of pleasure-sucking has

now brought to our notice two of the decisive characteristics of infantile sexuality. It appears in connection
with the satisfaction of the great organic needs, and it
behaves *autoerotically,* that is to say, it seeks and finds its
objects in its own person. What is most clearly discerni-
ble in regard to the taking of nourishment is to some
extent repeated with the process of excretion. We conclude that infants experience pleasure in the evacuation
of urine and the contents of the bowels, and that they
very soon endeavor to contrive these actions so that the
accompanying excitation of the membranes in these
erotogenic zones may secure them the maximum possible
gratification. As Lou Andreas has pointed out, with fine
intuition, the outer world first steps in as a hindrance
at this point, a hostile force opposed to the child's desire
for pleasure—the first hint he receives of external and
internal conflicts to be experienced later on. He is not
to pass his excretions whenever he likes but at times ap-
pointed by other people. To induce him to give up these
sources of pleasure he is told that everything connected
with these functions is "improper," and must be kept
concealed. In this way he is first required to exchange
pleasure for value in the eyes of others. His own attitude
to the excretions is at the outset very different. His own
feces produce no disgust in him; he values them as part
of his own body and is unwilling to part with them, he
uses them as the first "present" by which he can mark
out those people whom he values especially. Even after
education has succeeded in alienating him from these
tendencies, he continues to feel the same high regard for
his "presents" and his "money"; while his achievements
in the way of urination appear to be the subject of particular pride.

I know that for some time you have been longing to

interrupt me with cries of: "Enough of these monstrosities! The motions of the bowels a source of pleasurable
sexual satisfaction exploited even by infants! Feces a
substance of great values and the anus a kind of genital
organ! We do not believe it; but we understand why
children's physicians and educationists have emphatically
rejected psychoanalysis and its conclusions!" Not at all;
you have merely forgotten for the moment that I have
been endeavoring to show you the connection between
the actual facts of infantile sexual life and the actual
facts of the sexual perversions. Why should you not know
that in many adults, both homosexual and heterosexual,
the anus actually takes over the part played by the
vagina in sexual intercourse? And that there are many
persons who retain the pleasurable sensations accompanying evacuations of the bowels throughout life and
describe them as far from insignificant? You may hear
from children themselves, when they are a little older
and able to talk about these things, what an interest they
take in the act of defecation and what pleasure they find
in watching others in the act. Of course if you have
previously systematically intimidated these children they
will understand very well that they are not to speak of
such things. And for all else that you refuse to believe I
refer you to the evidence brought out in analysis and to
the direct observation of children and I tell you that it
will require the exercise of considerable ingenuity to
avoid seeing all this or to see it in a different light. Nor
am I at all averse from your thinking the relationship
between childish sexual activities and the sexual perversions positively striking. It is a matter of course that
there should be this relationship; for if a child has a
sexual life at all it must be of a perverted order, since
apart from a few obscure indications he is lacking in all

that transforms sexuality into the reproductive function. Moreover, it is a characteristic common to all the perversions that in them reproduction as an aim is put aside. This is actually the criterion by which we judge whether a sexual activity is perverse—if it departs from reproduction in its aims and pursues the attainment of gratification independently. You will understand therefore that the gulf and turning point in the development of the sexual life lies at the point of its subordination to the purposes of reproduction. Everything that occurs before this conversion takes place, and everything which refuses to conform to it and serves the pursuit of gratification alone, is called by the unhonored title of "perversion" and as such is despised.

So let me continue my brief account of infantile sexuality. I could supplement what I have told you concerning two of the bodily systems by extending the same scrutiny to the others. The sexual life of the child consists entirely in the activities of a series of component-instincts which seek for gratification independently of one another, some in his own body and others already in an external object. Among the organs of these bodily systems the genitalia rapidly take the first place; there are people in whom pleasurable gratification in their own genital organ, without the aid of any other genital organ or object, is continued without interruption from the onanism habitual in the suckling period of infancy to the onanism of necessity occurring in the years of puberty, and then maintained indefinitely beyond that. Incidentally, the subject of onanism is not so easily exhausted; it contains material for consideration from various angles.

In spite of my wish to limit the extent of this discussion I must still say something about sexual curiosity in children. It is too characteristic of childish sexuality and too important for the symptom-formation of the neuroses to be omitted. Infantile sexual curiosity begins very early, sometimes before the third year. It is not connected with the difference between the sexes, which is nothing to children, since they—boys, at least—ascribe the same male genital organ to both sexes. If then a boy discovers the vagina in a little sister or playmate he at once tries to deny the evidence of his senses; for he cannot conceive of a human being like himself without his most important attribute. Later, he is horrified at the possibilities it reveals to him; the influence of previous threats occasioned by too great a preoccupation with his own little member now begins to be felt. He comes under the dominion of the castration complex, which will play such a large part in the formation of his character if he remains healthy, and of his neurosis if he falls ill, and of his resistances if he comes under analytic treatment. Of little girls we know that they feel themselves heavily handicapped by the absence of a large visible penis and envy the boy's possession of it; from this source primarily springs the wish to be a man which is resumed again later in the neurosis, owing to some maladjustment to a female development. The clitoris in the girl, moreover, is in every way equivalent during childhood to the penis; it is a region of especial excitability in which autoerotic satisfaction is achieved. In the transition to womanhood very much depends upon the early and complete relegation of this sensitivity from the clitoris over to the vaginal orifice. In those women who are sexually anesthetic, as it is called, the clitoris has stubbornly retained this sensitivity.

The sexual interest of children is primarily directed to the problem of birth—the same problem that lies behind the riddle of the Theban Sphinx. This curiosity is for the most part aroused by egoistic dread of the arrival of another child. The answer which the nursery has ready for the child, that the stork brings the babies, meets with incredulity even in little children much more often than we imagine. The feeling of having been deceived by grown-up people, and put off with lies, contributes greatly to a sense of isolation and to the development of independence. But the child is not able to solve this problem on his own account. His undeveloped sexual constitution sets definite limits to his capacity to understand it. He first supposes that children are made by mixing some special thing with the food taken; nor does he know that only women can have children. Later, he learns of this limitation and gives up the idea of children being made by food, though it is retained in fairy tales. A little later he soon sees that the father must have something to do with making babies, but he cannot discover what it is. If by chance he is witness of the sexual act he conceives it as an attempt to overpower the woman, as a combat, the sadistic misconception of coitus; at first, however, he does not connect this act with the creation of children; if he discovers blood on the mother's bed or underlinen he takes it as evidence of injury inflicted by the father. In still later years of childhood he probably guesses that the male organ of the man plays an essential part in the procreation of children, but cannot ascribe to this part of the body any function but that of urination.

Children are all united from the outset in the belief that the birth of a child takes place by the bowel; that is to say, that the baby is produced like a piece of feces. Not until all interest has been weaned from the anal region is this theory abandoned and replaced by the supposition that the navel opens, or that the area between the two nipples is the birthplace of the child. In some such manner as this the enquiring child approaches some knowledge of the facts of sex, unless, misled by his ignorance, he overlooks them until he receives an imperfect and discrediting account of them, usually in the period before puberty, which not infrequently affects him traumatically.

Now you will probably have heard that the term "sexual" has suffered an unwarrantable expansion of meaning at the hands of psychoanalysis, in order that its assertions regarding the sexual origin of the neuroses and the sexual significance of the symptoms may be maintained. You can now judge for yourselves whether this amplification is justified or not. We have extended the meaning of the concept "sexuality" only so far as to include the sexual life of perverted persons and also of children; that is to say, we have restored to it its true breadth of meaning. What is called sexuality outside psychoanalysis applies only to the restricted sexual life that is subordinated to the reproductive function and is called normal.

2.
The Sexual Impulse in Childhood

by *Havelock Ellis*

Toward the end of his amazingly productive career, the noted pioneer sexologist responded to a demand for a concise introduction to sex psychology by summarizing the seven volumes of his monumental *Studies in the Psychology of Sex* in a smaller work which he subtitled "A Manual for Students." The selection that follows contains a critical, but friendly, analysis of Freudian views concerning the first appearance of the sexual impulse and, centering on the problem of masturbation, carries the examination forward through prepubertal and youthful sexuality. Reprinted from *Psychology of Sex* by Havelock Ellis, copyright, 1933, by Havelock Ellis, by permission of Emerson Books, Inc.

See also Chapter 2 in *Women*: "Prepuberty in Woman."

The First Appearance of the Sexual Impulse

IT USED TO BE BELIEVED that in childhood the sex impulse had no existence at all. That belief was not so common as some have supposed. But if it is possible to maintain that the sex impulse has no normal existence in early life, then every manifestation of it at that period must be "perverse," and even Freud, who regards infantile sexuality as normal, also regards it as "perverse," as he phrases it, "polymorph-perverse." In any discussion of the matter, however brief, it is essential to clear up this confusion.

It must be said at the outset that what may fairly be termed manifestations of the sexual impulse—even when we do not adopt a wide extension of the term "sexual"—

are undoubtedly much more frequent than was formerly supposed. There is also a much greater range in their force, their precocity, and their nature than has been commonly suspected.

Even in the primary and initial aptitude of the genital organs for sexual stimulation there is a fundamental range of variation. The aptitude of some infants at an early age to manifest genital reactions, which were usually regarded as reflex signs of irritation, was long ago a familiar observation. Such manifestations do not persist in memory, so that we have no direct evidence as to whether or not they are pleasurable, but many persons of both sexes can recall agreeable sensations connected with the genital organs in childhood; they are not (as is sometimes imagined) repressed; what is repressed, and usually indeed not experienced, is the impulse to mention them to grown-up persons, and they are commonly not mentioned to anyone. But they tend to persist in memory because they stand out of relation to ordinary experience and in striking contrast to it.

Definite sexual self-excitement has long been known to occur at an early age. Early in the nineteenth century various authors in France and elsewhere—Marc, Fonssagrives, Perez, etc.—gave cases of children of both sexes who masturbated from the age of three or four. Robie found that in boys the first sex feelings occur between the ages of five and fourteen, in girls between eight and nineteen; in both boys and girls these first manifestations more frequently appear during the later than the earlier years. Hamilton, in his more carefully detailed inquiry, has found that 20 per cent males and 14 per cent females find pleasure in their sex organs before the age of six. Katharine Davis, comparing groups of men and women, found that 20.9 per cent boys began to masturbate up to and including the age of eleven, and 49.1 per cent girls, though during the next three years the percentage of boys was much in excess of the girls. It is a mistake to suppose that all children experience, or are capable of experiencing, genital excitement or pleasurable sexual sensations. Crucial cases occur in which the child, innocently led away by another child who gives assurance that friction will favor the development of the penis in size, will in this innocence sedulously try to procure the supposed benefit but without attaining in any degree either genital reaction or sensory pleasure, although in due course at puberty, if not before, the organ becomes fully excitable. There is thus a wide range of genital and sexual aptitude in childhood. How far the differences are due to definitely different hereditary antecedents it is not always easy to say. On the whole it would appear, as we should expect, that the child of sound and solid ancestry is less sexually excitable in childhood, and the child of more unsound heredity or of hypersexual parents more precociously excitable. This is definitely suggested by Dr. Hamilton's inquiries which indicate that the later sex life begins the more satisfactory marriage turns out.

The subject becomes more complex when we go beyond localized genital phenomena of sex. And here we encounter the *libido* of the psychoanalysts. In early days that met with violent opposition when applied to infancy and childhood, nor can it be said that the opposition has been entirely overcome. It is now recognized, however, that much depends on the way in which we define the term *libido*. Like many Freudian terms, it was not happily chosen, and it is not easy to dissociate it from the English term "libidinous." Jung, the most distinguished psychoanalyst outside the Freudian school, dissociates libido, indeed, from any special connection with sex and takes it in a wide sense as "psychic energy" corresponding to the *"élan vital"* of Bergson, or, in English, "vital urge," which is the term some people would like to use, for there is no doubt that we cannot dissociate the term "libido" from definitely sex energy. Freud has wavered in his view of *libido* and its development. As he remarks in his illuminating essay on the "Infantile Organization of the Libido" (1923), at one time he emphasized its early pregenital organization, though later he came to accept a close approximation of the sexuality of childhood to adult sexuality. But the infantile genital organization, he goes on to say, really involves the primacy of the phallus, which he regards as the only genital organ recognized in childhood. At the same time he speaks of a "pregenital" phase and asserts that "not until puberty does the polarity of sexuality coincide with *male* and *female.*" Some have detected here an undue tendency to theoretic generalization in a world which consists of individuals, each with a different heredity, and naturally also with a different mode of reaction to the external world. But the main point is that, for Freud, sexual polarity is only attained at puberty. Therefore, since for the ordinary person "libidinousness" mainly rests on sexual polarity, the Freudian *libido* scarcely seems to call for any excessive horror. It is the Freudian terminology which is at fault. We may agree with Ernest Jones that if we divide sex activity into two phases of "initial pleasures" and "end pleasures," "the manifestations before puberty are almost entirely confined to the former group." We must, however, admit exceptions.

Freud's conception of the *libido* would have met with less opposition if he had at the outset taken up the position which at last he took in 1925 *(Das Ich und das Es)* when, more or less discarding *libido,* he set forth the relationship of the *ego* to the *id* (the term by which *es* has been ingeniously translated), the *id* being the more or less unconscious and primitive self with its passions, and the *ego* the more conscious and reasonable self in closer reaction with the outer world, which gradually develops out of the *id* and separates itself off from it. As Freud himself remarks, this conception fairly well corresponds with popular and generally accepted ideas.

When we survey widely the activities of children it would not seem that it is generally "the primacy of the phallus" which we find most striking (most of those familiar with babies would say that it is the primacy of the thumb and toes), and so far as it is, it is often (as indeed Freud remarks) essentially an impulse of curiosity, which some mothers unfortunately repress and so drive in and unduly emphasize. Here are the most "curious" parts of the body, the parts (with fingers and toes) that for a child are most like playthings. This interest may lead on to pleasurable sensation, but for most children it would appear that what may be regarded as sexual sensation is outside the genital sphere, being sexual sensation of the threshold, that is to say sensation of a kind that would in an adult lie on the threshold of the sexual sphere and lead up to it (thus legitimately belonging to the art of love). The difference is that such sensations in the child, while pleasurable, do not usually pass over the threshold of the actual sexual sensation.

Such phenomena are in the first place most usually in the oral region. This we should expect, as the most acute pleasure of the infant could scarcely fail to be derived from the sensitive lips of the mouth in contact with the milk-yielding nipple of the mother. Since the mouth is an erogenic or sexually stimulating zone in adult life we cannot be surprised that it should be a pleasure-

center on the sexual threshold even in infancy. Thumb-
sucking sometimes becomes a substitute for nipple-suck-
ing when it is unattainable or outgrown; it is held by
some—although the opinion is disputed by numerous
authorities—that in predisposed children this may be a
kind of masturbation and later lead on to ordinary masturbation. It is a practice found among a considerable
and varying proportion of young children of both sexes
and may even begin immediately after birth.

Only second to the emergence of the oral center is
probably the anal center. As long as the motions are
passed automatically and without restraint there is little
opportunity for the anal region to become a pleasure
center. But as soon as any restraint is imposed gratification in the discharges is certain to be felt and the pleasurable sensitivity of the anus is liable to become developed; it is often in later years an erogenic zone, though
not so often or so profoundly as the oral region in the
adult. It is held by some psychoanalysts that at an early
age there is in some subjects a tendency to retain the
feces with a pleasure aim, and that such a tendency is
significant for later psychic development; this, however,
has been denied by others as not easy to prove. Much
the same may be said of the urinary discharge, though
here the pleasure, alike in the infant and the adults, is
more exclusively in the discharge itself, and some observers note that the infant may find pleasure in bestow-
ing this discharge on a specially preferred person, though
it is quite likely that this is often a misinterpretation of
the facts, and that the discharge of urine in the infant
under the influence of pleasurable emotion may be no
more intentional than it is in the adult woman in whom
it occasionally occurs by reflex action, and to her great
vexation, during the sexual orgasm. Hamilton remarks

that 21 per cent men and 16 per cent women admit being interested in urine or playing with it in early life, and exactly the same percentage as regards feces.

On the psychic side there is even less doubt of the liability of children to experience emotions which may fairly be called sexual than there is on the physical side. Many years ago Sanford Bell showed, on a collective basis, the frequency of these manifestations, which all have had occasions to observe sometimes. His report may still be read with profit. He had studied the question for fifteen years, both in and out of schools, and personally observed 800 cases, while he had obtained records of 1,700 other cases (thus 2,500 in all) from 360 other observers of whom only five could recall no experience of that kind from their own childhood, a fact which indicates that it is a mistake to suppose that repression of such early experiences is common; when repression occurs it is evidently abnormal and probably due to inborn peculiarities. Bell found that emotion of this kind may be witnessed as early as the middle of the third year, and that in the nature of its manifestations there tend to be several stages of which the first usually continues to the age of eight, and the second to the age of fourteen. In the first stage the boy is usually more modest and less aggressive than the girl. The emotion is detected by a number of little signs which it is difficult to avoid assigning to sex origin. A tendency to hug and kiss is common but does not always occur, and there is frequently a desire to conceal the emotion from its object and from anyone else. While some form of touch contact is frequently sought it is not generally specifically sexual, and when it is Bell was inclined to regard the case as precocious. The erethism, as he well remarks, is not usually (though it may be) manifested in the sex organs, but it is distributed throughout the entire body, especially the vascular and nervous systems. Spring is the period of the year when these manifestations are most likely to occur.

Students of childhood, psychoanalytic and others, have since confirmed and elaborated these observations. Freud has again and again dealt with the matter, and Oskar Pfister, in his extensive and discursive work on love in children and its defects of development, comes to the conclusion that there is an amazing and unsuspected multiplicity of manifestations in the love sentiments of children.

It is, as already indicated, characteristic of the sexual or pseudosexual interests of children that they should mainly fall outside the sphere which for the adult is that of sex proper, partly because on the physical side the genital centers are still undeveloped and partly because on the psychic side the opposite sex has not yet usually acquired the definite significance which after puberty sooner or later it possesses.

An interesting and often overlooked trait of childish sexuality is algolagnia, or a pleasurable interest in pain, this including pleasure in the witnessing of pain, the inflicting of pain, or the experiencing of it. Various adult names are commonly applied to these manifestations such as "cruelty," "sadism," "masochism," etc., and this is probably inevitable because it is only so that adults can explain to themselves these manifestations of the childish psyche. But they are misleading and unfortunate for they are far away from the aims of childhood. The child has not, for instance, yet formulated the humanely adult notion of "cruelty," and when we remember that even for many adults it has no clear existence we cannot be surprised that it is alien to the children who amiably and pleasantly witness the sufferings of the lower animals and often themselves increase or cause them. Children are at work—or, if you wish, at play—in the exercise-ground of inquisitive reason and as yet undifferentiated emotion: the fossilized rules of adult morality are here misplaced. It is the function of education, in the proper sense of that term (for the fallacy that education means *putting in* and not *bringing out* is still common among the ignorant), to help the child to educe in due course the activities of later life, and to make clear to him, as soon as his comprehension permits, that his own early unrestrained impulses do not work in the adult world. The fact that we are here primarily concerned with exercises in the field of emotion, only incidentally liable to reach the threshold of pain, is shown in the child's equal or greater liking to suffer its infliction. Games of "punishment" with much reciprocal smacking have always been privately popular among children of both sexes, perhaps especially girls, the hairbrush often being used for this purpose. Self-flagellation is also sometimes practiced, and even after puberty, when the genital centers are fully active, it may be adopted by either sex to heighten the solitary pleasure of the sexual impulse in the absence of a person of the opposite sex. Daydreams of torture are a not uncommon source of pleasure even among young children, and at a rather later age one has heard of Foxe's *Book of Martyrs* proving a source of thrilling delight. Sometimes the child experiences an irresistible impulse to inflict pain on himself and often on his penis, which indicates that, even if not a source of sexual excitement in the adult sense, the penis is already a center of emotional interest. Such facts recall the castration-complex to which some psychoanalysts attach enormous importance. A string may be strongly tied round the penis; or it may even be violently struck; and the case has lately been recorded of a girl of nine who tied a thread round her clitoris and was unable to remove it, so that surgical interference became necessary. Sensation and emotion are still in a comparatively diffused and as it were uncrystallized form. As the realization of pain is so early necessary in life for self-preservation it is inevitable that painful emotions should be those in which the still vague pleasure impulses tend to take shape. Hamilton found that among his subjects, who may all be said to be of high character and culture, only 49 per cent men and 68 per cent women never experience pleasure in inflicting pain; while nearly 30 per cent of both men and women had had pleasure in experiencing pain.

How far we are here from adult developments is shown by the now well recognized fact that neither similarity of sex nor closeness of blood relationship provides any bar to these manifestations. The adult who succeeds in discerning the occurrence of such manifestations begins to talk solemnly and pedantically of "homosexuality" and "incest" and the "Oedipus complex," without realizing the absurdity he is perpetrating. He would indeed be speaking quite rationally if he were dealing with the like phenomena in his own grown-up world. There can be no homosexuality when there is yet no conception of sexuality, and no incest before the barriers of relationship are known. As a distinguished psychoanalyst, Dr. Jelliffe, has said of this manner of labeling the impulsive activity of childhood, "expressing it in terms of conscious adult activity is nonsense." Even apart from sex, the best psychologists of childhood (like Stern in his *Psychology of Early Childhood*) are trying to make clear that we must not measure children by our psychic powers, but learn to understand their different natures. Until we have realized this, until we have cleared away the elaborate structure of childhood sexuality erected on the adult pattern by adults who seem to have lost all memory of youth, we shall wander among vain shadows in this field. Here certainly is a kingdom of knowledge into which only those can enter who become as little children.

At this point it is necessary to refer to a psychological trait to which psychoanalysts, above all Freud, who first called attention to it, have in the past, and to some extent still, attached supreme importance: the so-called Oedipus complex. It is not, on the surface, quite happily so called, for what we hereby mean psychologically is simply an attraction of love (a "wish to marry") the parent of opposite sex, on the part of the young child, with a corresponding jealousy of the parent of the same sex, whereas in the myth Oedipus experienced no such feelings, but was compelled by the oracle and the gods to marry his mother and kill his father unwittingly, in spite of all his own struggles to avoid these crimes; but this opposition Freud explains away by saying that oracle and gods were a glorified embodiment of the Unconscious. Freud's Oedipus complex, when he first put it forward some thirty years ago—certainly in an incautious way and with a misapplied use of the word "incest"—was, as he frequently stated, greeted with horror and execration. That attitude, to one of his strong and combative temperament, merely aroused a more emphatic assertion of the doctrine. In some degree, in some form or another, even an inverted form, the Oedipus complex, Freud declared, "is a regular and very important factor in the mental life of the child." He went on to find that "it does not seem impossible" that the Oedipus complex is the source of all perversions and also "the actual nucleus of the neuroses." Rank, at the time closely as-

sociated with him, showed with the help of his wide
literary culture how frequently and variously this motive
had entered dramatic poetry. Finally in 1913, in *Totem
and Taboo,* Freud developed a conception of the Oedipus complex as lying at the root of primitive morality,
furnishing that sense of guilt which to Freud seems "the
ultimate source of religion and morality," the earliest
form of Kant's categorical imperative, and the first embodiment of the great cosmic figures, which, beginning
as Parents became God, Fate, Nature, what we will.

But the psychoanalysts who have thus placed the
Oedipus complex at the foundation of a large part of
human culture have failed to realize that that complex
can only be associated, if at all, with a particular family
constitution, and that the family, far from having only
one single form of constitution, has varied widely. A
patriarchal family, such as we have had during historical
times in the parts of Europe best known to us, is essential
for an Oedipus complex. But that is far from being a
kind of family always and everywhere known. The substance of the family is biological but its forms are socially
molded. This is made clear by Malinowski (who started
with a bias favorable to psychoanalysis) in his book *Sex
and Repression in Savage Society.* The complexes which
are supposed to mold culture could only have arisen
under culture, and cultures are of various kinds. Nor can
we accept a "primeval horde equipped with all the bias,
maladjustments and ill-tempers of a middle-class European family and then let loose in a prehistoric jungle."
Every type of civilization cannot but have a special type
of complex as its necessary by-product.

The Oedipus complex, further, rests on the belief that
there is a strong natural human tendency, appearing at
the earliest age, to sex love toward near relations which

can only be overcome by stern laws and severe repressions. It is agreed by all authorities that the free exercise of incestuous impulses is incompatible with a family order, and that on such a basis no developed culture would be likely to arise. But authorities differ as to the natural or unnatural character of incestuous impulses. Westermarck held originally that there is a definite natural instinct averse in incest; Freud holds that there is from infancy a strong natural instinct to incest; Malinowski does not accept the aversion to incest as natural but as introduced by culture, "a complex scheme of cultural reactions." The position I have long held largely harmonizes these opposing views. There is a sexual attraction toward persons with whom there is close contact, such persons being often relations, and the attraction being therefore termed "incestuous." But this is a weak attraction under normal circumstances (there are always exceptions) and is quickly overcome when a fascinating new object of desire from outside his own circle strikes the young beholder. There is no anti-incestuous instinct, no natural aversion, but a deep stirring of the sexual instinct needs a strong excitement, and for this a new object is required, not one that has become commonplace by familiarity. This is a view to which Westermarck shows himself favorable in the later edition of his great work on marriage and had previously been accepted by Crawley, as well as by Heape. It is clear to anyone who grasps the physiology of the sexual process and the psychology of courtship. A typical illustration may be quoted from Restif de la Bretonne's autobiography, *Monsieur Nicolas,* a precious document for erotic psychology. We here learn how an extremely precocious child was from the age of four in some degree sexually excitable by his female companions and playmates, though he received their caresses with much shyness. It was not till the age of eleven that he became highly aroused, even to the extent of attaining coitus, and losing all his early shyness, and this was with *a girl who was a stranger* and belonging to another village. Many bad theories might have been avoided had this psychological fact been clearly understood. There is no "aversion to incest," but under natural conditions a deep sexual attraction requires a powerful stimulus, and this cannot normally arise out of familiarity.

Various objections have been brought against my statement of the psychological basis of exogamy, but they are due to misunderstandings and also a failure to allow for many highly relevant considerations. Some critics have been misled by too exclusively thinking of the conditions among civilized man and domesticated animals. Some have failed to see that there is no question of absolute indifference to the sexual stimulus of familiar persons which may easily exist and sometimes indeed is peculiarly strong. Others have rightly insisted that incest is unlikely to produce the best offspring or to result in domestic peace, and that exogamy is a highly important factor in social evolution. These influences may very well be responsible for the incest-taboo and remained responsible for maintaining it. But they could hardly have arisen except upon the foundation and by the support of the undoubted psychic tendency to which I have called attention. Social institutions are never unnatural in origin; they can only arise on a natural basis. In primitive life, moreover, we find, as Crawley points out, a naive desire to assist Nature, as it were, by adding to what is normal the categorical imperative of custom and law.

Today we may look back serenely on the Oedipus complex and the ferocious reactions it seems to have evoked.

When the facts are viewed directly and simply, without any attempt to make them look either terrifying or grandiloquent, or to generalize them into universal doctrines, it is easy to discover the very natural fact that the young boy is attracted to his mother (the corresponding phenomenon is the attachment of the young girl to her father) and is jealous at first of what distracts his mother's attention away from him. Jealousy is an entirely natural primitive emotion; every dog is inclined to growl at a seeming attempt to share his bone; any cat may be displeased at the effort of a strange cat to share her plate. Many of us—even the most normal and least neurotic—can recall, or have been told, that in early childhood we disapproved at first of the appearance of a baby brother or sister. But we can also recall that in a very short time we were completely reconciled to the new phenomenon and were even proud to assist in lovingly tending it. Any feeling of hostility to the father seldom, under normal conditions, entered at any stage. The reason is fairly obvious. The baby is new and arouses new feelings; the father has been there from the first; nothing occurs to change the attitude toward him; he is accepted as a matter of course.

But, we see also, the situation is undoubtedly favorable to morbid and emotional developments in constitutionally neurotic subjects, especially under the influence of injudicious parental behavior, such as favoritism or careless neglect. We may then have the whole chain of manifestations described by psychoanalysts. It is necessary to be alive to these possibilities, and prepared to unravel such a case fearlessly, for the path of psychology cannot be followed except with courage. But it is not necessary to generalize from a single case or even from many cases. And it is fatal to all sound conclusions to set out with a predetermined pattern and to attempt to fit every case on to it.

All this is now becoming clearer and is beginning to be admitted even by psychoanalysts. Thus Rank, who was so active in developing the conception of the Oedipus complex in its early stages, twenty years later, in his suggestive work on *Modern Education* remarks that "the Oedipus complex, as the attraction to the parent of the opposite sex and jealousy of the parent of the same sex, is not so clearly found in practice as mythology represents it and as Freud at first believed," adding that it has not been easily possible even for psychoanalysts to maintain it. Elsewhere Rank observes that the famous "mother complex" is not so much a real fixation of the child on the mother as merely a sign of the prevalence today of the belief in the influence of the mother in the child's education.

The castration complex is associated by psychoanalysts with the Oedipus complex, Freud regarding it as primarily a reaction to intimidation in the field of sex, and any restraint on infantile activity being ultimately ascribed to the father. It sometimes happens that mothers and nurses, seeing the young child handling his penis, playfully threaten to cut it off, and the child may possibly take the threat seriously, especially if he observes that his sister has no penis; while the little girl may feel it a deprivation to lack an organ her brother possesses. It is not easy to assert that those feelings count for much in ordinary children, though Freud has gone so far as to claim, not only that the castration complex may play a large part in the formation of neuroses but even in the formation of character in the healthy child. That the castration complex is influential in some neurotic persons there can be no doubt. Some persons of keen intelligence but neurotic disposition, when able to review their early development, have found much significance in the influence upon them of foolish nurses in arousing a castration complex.

The definite manifestation that has always most prominently attracted attention in connection with this aspect of early life is that which from old time has been termed "masturbation." Here it is convenient and possibly legitimate to speak of *sexuality*, although it is not strictly correct, for we are concerned with an act which may, and often does, begin in a merely generalized and instinctive search for pleasurable sensations. But since it is an act that is not confined to early life but may occur at any age, often in connection with the most developed ideas of sex, it would be hypercritical to attempt to draw a line of distinction.

The ancient and common name of the act indicates the excitation of the sexual zone in either sex by means of the hand. But commonly and quite inevitably, the word is employed to cover all methods by which friction can be employed to produce pleasurable sensations in the genital sphere. No doubt the hand is the most frequent instrument and that which, in the absence of mental inhibitions and physical impediments, is most naturally employed. But there are many other ways: in boys, games, sports, gymnastics, even the accidental pressure of the clothes, may suffice, especially under condition of general erethism, to produce erection and even orgasm, frequently to the surprise, and sometimes the alarm or the horror, of the subject to whom this experience comes; states of tension and apprehension, and spectacles arousing emotions of horror or of pleasure, may produce the same results, as well as actual experience of a similar kind, such as the punishment of whip-

ping, the classical example of this being the experience
of young Rousseau at the hands of his governess, which
had, as he believed, a permanent influence on his highly
sensitive psychic disposition. In girls, the action of the
hands, though as in boys it is the most common method,
is even less essential; a casual contact of the sexual parts
may prove pleasurable even in the first childhood and be
one of a girl's earliest memories; later, contact and friction with external objects may be instinctively sought;
small girls will, without concealment, rub themselves
against the corner of a chair, or the handle of a chest of
drawers; young women will develop and continue a
similar habit and even be able to excite themselves
against the leg of a table at public restaurants. Without
any extraneous help at all, it is sometimes possible for a
girl to obtain excitement and orgasm by rubbing the
thighs together, or, when in a favorable emotional state,
by pressing them tightly together. And, as in boys, the
same results may occur almost or quite spontaneously,
under the influence of exciting spectacles or seductive
thoughts. This, we see, is hardly distinguishable from
what may happen, in a normal manner, between two
lovers.

In boys who have had no earlier spontaneous impulses
of sexual activity and no initiation from companions, the
first orgasm usually occurs at puberty during sleep, with
or without dreams, sometimes causing the boy much
anxiety or shame, until in the course of years he learns
to accept it as the almost inevitable accompaniment of
adult life when it is being lived continently. In girls,
however, it is not inevitable under similar conditions. It
is rare (as I have frequently pointed out though the
statement has not always been accepted) for girls to have

their *first* experience of sexual excitement (with or without orgasm) in sleep, and the supposition that they commonly do is due to ignorance. The boy awakes sexually in sleep, spontaneously. The girl must be actively awakened, by others or herself, though after that, even if it may not occur until long after she has reached adult age, she will be liable to experience the most vivid erotic dreams. We probably have here an interesting psychic sexual difference, the greater sexual activity of the male, the greater sexual quiescence of the female, which does not, however, mean superior sexuality of the male, or inferior sexual needs of the female; it may be indeed the reason why the girl is more liable to hysterical and other nervous symptoms, if we regard these as manifestations of latent sexual energy.

Robie, in America, among a large number of persons of both sexes found few or none who had not had experience of masturbation or other form of autoerotic activity at some period of their lives and often before the age of eight. His observations were not always very precise. Dr. Katharine Davis, who gave special attention to this point, found, among 1,000 American college women above the age of twenty-two, that 60 per cent gave definite histories of masturbation. She investigated the whole question, perhaps with more thoroughness and in greater detail than any other worker. Among unmarried college women graduates she found that 43.6 per cent began the practice from the third to the tenth years inclusive; 20.2 per cent from eleven to fifteen inclusive; 13.9 per cent from sixteen to twenty-two inclusive; 15.5 per cent from twenty-three to twenty-nine inclusive. Comparing her results with those of other investigators dealing with men the results are as follows:

	Men	Women
Up to and including 11 yrs........	20.9	49.1
Up to and including 12-14 yrs.....	44.3	14.6
Up to and including 15-17 yrs......	30.3	6.2
Up to 18 yrs. and over............	4.5	30.1

These results carry weight because the groups include about 500 men to about 900 women. They show, to an unexpected degree, that girls masturbate early more often than boys, and that during adolescence it is the boys who largely predominate, while after adult age is reached, as we should anticipate, women are in a large majority.

Dr. Hamilton, in his careful study of 100 married men and 100 married women of good social standing, found that 97 per cent of the men and 74 per cent of the women had at some period masturbated. These results are fairly in accordance with the more general conclusion of Moll, whose work on *The Sexual Life of the Child* (1908) was the earliest comprehensive study of the subject and is still among the most judicious. Moll remarks, however, that masturbation is not as common as is sometimes supposed in Germany, and I may add that it seems not so common in England or even in France as the American percentage might lead us to anticipate.

It will be seen that these manifestations extend far beyond the classic conception of "masturbation" in its literal and commonly accepted sense, which cannot really be said to constitute a separate group for it blends with the larger group without definite frontiers.

When we thus view this group of manifestations as a whole it is seen why we cannot properly term them "perverse." They are natural; they are the inevitable result of the action of the sexual impulse when working in the absence of the object of sexual desire, occurring, under such conditions, even in some of the lower animals; and they are emphatically natural when they occur before adult age. It is natural also that they should occur in adult age when the sexual urge seems irresistible and when normal sexual approaches are undesired or undesirable, although, it must be added, it is equally natural when, under such circumstances, they are inhibited or repressed by other considerations which may seem of a superior order.

It is instructive to explore the attitude toward prepubertal and youthful sexuality in different stages of culture and different periods of history. When we are concerned with an impulse so primitive and fundamental as that of sex we cannot decide what is "natural" and what is "perverse" merely by the standard set up in accordance with shifting fashions of thought, the religious or social customs of one particular age. Least of all can it be said that the age we are ourselves emerging from, with its peculiar and highly colored views of sex, furnishes any universal standard.

Let us, for instance, turn to almost the only race of a culture outside our own traditions which has yet been studied with scientific care, the Trobrianders of New Guinea, as represented in Malinowski's *Sexual Life of Savages*. Children in the Trobriand Islands possess a freedom and independence which extends to sexual matters. No special precautions are taken, or would easily be possible, to prevent children seeing their parents in sexual intercourse or from hearing discussion of sexual matters, though their elders think highly of children who do not repeat what they may thus hear or see. On fishing expeditions, when girls follow their fathers, it is usual for the men to remove the public fig leaf, so that the shape of the male body is never a mystery for the girls.

Both boys and girls receive instruction in sexual matters
from slightly older companions, and from an early age
play at sex games, which enable them to gain some
knowledge of these matters and to gratify natural curiosity, even to obtain a certain amount of pleasure; the
hand and the mouth are commonly used for genital
manipulations in these games. Little girls usually begin
to play at sex at four or five years, and real sex life may
begin from between the age of six and eight, while for
the boys it begins between ten and twelve. The ordinary
round games played by boys and girls in the center of
the village have at times a strong flavor of sex. The
grownups regard all these manifestations as natural, and
see no reason to scold or interfere. No harm comes of it,
not even illegitimate children, though how this is prevented remains a mystery. The young Trobrianders pal-
liate crude sexuality by the help of a poetic instinct, and
show indeed, Malinowski remarks, "a great sense of the
singular and the romantic in their games."

There are, however, widely different attitudes toward
sex even in the same part of the world and among people not very widely separated in culture and race. Margaret Mead, in *Growing Up in New Guinea*, describes
the Manus people of the Admiralty Islands to the north
of New Guinea as extremely puritanic. They regard sex
with aversion and excretions with disgust, repressing and
avoiding their manifestations and seeking the maximum
of secrecy. The children, though carefully trained in
physical respects, are otherwise treated with extreme indulgence and left free; but sexual manifestations, including masturbation, are slight and infrequent, because
there are few opportunities for isolation. There seemed
to be much sexual frigidity, and the married women do
not admit pleasure in married life and seek to avoid

sexual intercourse, nor are there any signs of romantic affection.

Another picture of youthful sex life outside our own culture, though this time not untouched by our civilization, is presented by Margaret Mead in *Coming of Age in Samoa*. Here our civilization has had a considerable dissolving influence on the old Samoan culture, so that what might seem a new and artificial culture has grown up and with considerable rapidity. Yet it has grown up naturally on what is evidently the foundation of the old Samoan culture, deprived of all but the minimum of its taboos and restrictions, and it seems to work beneficially. Small boys and girls tend to avoid each other, not by external command but by custom and instinct; yet from the earliest age, owing to the general absence of privacy, they begin to be familiar with the essential facts of life and death, including the details of sex and sexual intercourse. They also have an individual sex life from childhood; nearly every little girl masturbates from the age of six or seven, more or less in secret, the boys also, but more usually in groups, and casual homosexual practices are common; on the part of growing girls or women working together such casual relationships are regarded as "a pleasant and natural diversion, just tinged with the salacious." Such "perversions" are neither banned nor cultivated into institutions; they are simply the sign of the recognition of a wide range of normality, and public opinion, while viewing attention to the details of sex as unseemly, does not regard them as wrong. . . .

When we turn to the European tradition, and to the sources of our modern civilization, the earliest references to these manifestations show no clearly implied disapproval or at the most an occasional touch of contempt, and there is even in Greek literature an association of

masturbation with gods. In historical times we find that
admired philosophers of the Cynic school boasted of the
advantages of satisfying sexual needs in a solitary manner. In Rome there appears to have been a considerable
amount of indifference to these matters, and even in the
Christian Church, for over a thousand years, there were
so many extravagant sexual excesses to combat that the
spontaneous solitary manifestations of sex scarcely attracted attention. It was not till the Reformation and at
first mainly in Protestant countries, though the movement quickly spread to France and other Catholic countries, that moralists and physicians began to be much
troubled about masturbation. This was in the eighteenth
century. At the same time opportunity was furnished to
quacks to offer more or less fantastic remedies for the
evils which were beginning to be attributed to "self-
abuse." Even until the end of the last century serious
physicians frequently took for granted that some grave
result or other might be induced by masturbation.

It was during the second half of the nineteenth century, when a new biological conception, under the inspiration of Darwin, was slowly permeating medicine,
that the idea of infantile and youthful "perversion" began to be undermined; on the one hand the new scientific study of sex, started by the pioneering work of
Krafft-Ebing at the end of the third quarter of the century, showed how common are such so-called "perversions" in early life while, on the other hand, the conception of evolution began to make it clear that we must
not apply developed adult standards to undeveloped
creatures, what is natural at one stage not necessarily
being natural at the previous stage.

An early representative of these influences was the
Italian psychiatrist Silvio Venturi, who belonged to the

Positivist school which sought in Italy to fertilize medicine with the new biological and social conceptions; he published in 1892 his elaborate study, *Le Degenerazioni Psicosessuali,* as exhibited in the individual and in social history, a work wherein various large and fruitful conceptions were thrown out. Venturi regarded sexual development as a slow process, not properly to be termed "sexual" until puberty, yet made up of separate factors which began at the beginning of life their separate development (infantile erections being such a factor and the later erotic sensibility of the lips being similarly developed in early life by nonerotic exercise) before they combine, after puberty, to constitute what may properly be termed sexuality, or, as Venturi, insisting on the psychic element termed it, *amore.* Masturbation (onanism, as Venturi always terms it) is regarded as "the germ of what later will be love." It appears in early youth, having its rudimentary roots in infancy, simply as a physical pleasure, without erotic imagery, as the satisfaction of an unknown and indeterminate organic need, certainly of sexual nature, but appearing to consciousness more like the action of scratching a sensory surface that itches, though the psychic condiment of forbidden fruit may be added to its enjoyment. The act is gradually complicated by psychic elements and genuinely erotic stimuli which slowly approximate it to an act of coitus with an hallucinatory mate, and it thus passes almost insensibly into adult sexual love, so disappearing, or else in a more retarded way which varies with the individual. Its elements, however, such as those that are fetishistic, are retained, by arrest of development, as Venturi states (following Lombroso and in accordance with the views of today), to constitute what in adult age, when carried so far as to replace the normal aim of sex, is described as a perversion. As Freud subsequently expressed it: "Perverted sexuality is nothing but infantile sexuality"; that is to say what is normal in the child may become abnormal when it occurs in the adult. Masturbation, thus, Venturi concludes, far from being the vice combated by teachers and moralists, is "the natural passage by which is reached the warm and generous love of youth and later the calm and positive matrimonial love of maturity."

Bibliography

A. Moll, *The Sexual Life of the Child.*

Sanford Bell, "The Emotion of Love between the Sexes," *American Journal of Psychology,* July, 1902.

Oskar Pfister, *Love in Children.*

Katharine B. Davis, *Factors in the Sex Life of Twenty-two Hundred Women.*

G. V. Hamilton, *A Research in Marriage.*

B. Malinowski, *Sexual Life of Savages.*

Margaret Mead, *Coming of Age in Samoa; Growing Up in New Guinea.*

3.
Youth and Sex: The Hot-Bloods

by Dorothy Dunbar Bromley and
Florence Haxton Britten

In their important survey of the sexual codes and conduct of
1300 college men and women, Bromley and Britten achieved
depth and vivid animation of their conclusions by permitting
the subjects of the study to speak for themselves. Of the six
composite types that emerged, The Hot-Bloods, those young
men who were most active in pursuit of sex experience, are
presented here. Reprinted from *Youth and Sex, A Study of 1300
College Students* by Dorothy Dunbar Bromley and Florence Hax-
ton Britten, copyright, 1938, by Harper & Brothers, by permission
of Dorothy Dunbar Bromley and the publisher.

See also Chapter 3 in *Women: "Youth and Sex: The Sowers of
Wild Oats."*

THE MALE FLIRT was a stock character in the theater
and literature of fifty years ago. In checked suit and
curling black mustache he leered at young girls and laid
traps for their seduction. Modern realism and frank discussion of sex and morals have deflated him and he lies
forgotten along with dudes, carpetbaggers, and other out-
moded figures.

The basic human pattern represented by the male flirt
has by no means disappeared, however. He caricatured
a primary male type, the huntsman. Instinct for the
hunt differentiates more objectively than anything else
that half of the men undergraduates who had had sexual
intercourse.

The typical nonvirgin undergraduate had had intercourse with four girls according to the accounts given by

307 nonvirgin men students in questionnaires and interviews. The Moderates, the three-fifths of this group
which rated below the median figure, reported for the
most part relations with one to four girls each. The Hot-
Bloods, the two-fifths which exceeded the median, recorded relations with from five to fifty girls each. A few
individuals in this group may have been discriminating
or have become so, but, by and large, the boys who had
had at the median age of twenty, relations with five or
more girls, classified as Hot-Bloods with individual variations.

Some seventeen men substituted large vague adjectives
for figures—"innumerable," "plenty,"—or they said,
"never counted"; "can't remember them all." Only a
dozen men appeared in the top brackets, claiming twenty to fifty girls each. Some may have exaggerated. It
would be consistent with their type. They were so few,
however, that their accuracy would not particularly affect
the general picture of undergraduate sex life which
emerges from the study.

The Hot-Bloods in many respects conformed to the
general pattern of the other groups. They were swept
by the same fads in clothes, sports, hobbies. They divided
in about the same proportions between East and West,
North and South. A majority came from middle-class
homes, attended public schools, considered their parents
happily married, but—and this is an interesting exception—only 15 per cent stated that their parents judged
conduct from a religious viewpoint. This gave the Hot-
Bloods the lowest proportion of religious parents in the
study, and less than half that of the virgins.

They contradicted popular ideas about the traditional
figure, the male flirt, who was usually a "city slicker"
dazzling simple village girls with his wiles. According to

the boys' records, it is still the village girls who fall an easy prey, but, it is the village boys who seduce them. Villages of 1,000 to 5,000 population had the highest proportion of boys who had indulged in precollege intercourse, 37 per cent as compared with 31 per cent for the entire group.

Failure of the village to provide interests and occupations for leisure-time activities may account for these figures. Cities large and small are building increasingly elaborate equipment for young people—gymnasia, swimming pools, playgrounds, clubs. The villages probably do less for their young people than any other type of community. In default of organized interests, village youths apparently fall back on the instinctive preoccupation of adolescence.

The differences revealed by the questionnaires between the Hot-Bloods and the other groups were few but significant, and centered around their behavior before entering college. The pattern which was to dominate their college life was already evident in high school. This is not to imply that they all remained true to type. Young men of college age are subject to countless whims and influences. Some highly promiscuous men changed suddenly to Moderates, after they had fallen in love or, more prosaically, contracted a disease. Whether they will stay changed or whether the original pattern will reassert itself is a question which did not come within the time limits of this study.

The Hot-Blood is comparatively uninhibited by the processes of civilization. He is young for his years. Whereas the men in both Moderate and Virgin groups showed keen interest in our study, criticized it pro and con and commented on the questionnaire, the Hot-Bloods as a rule seemed chiefly interested in their own exploits. The

more provocative quotations in this chapter were exceptional and were selected as being more articulate and
illuminating than the average.

The Hot-Bloods were highly suggestible. They generally took for granted the position that continence was
an impracticable or stupid idea. They considered it an
intolerable strain or wrote with frank simplicity, "have
never tried it." Some seemed sincerely puzzled by the
suggestion of possible standards of sexual behavior. They
said that they saw no purpose in self-denial if they could
find a girl who was willing. A man of twenty-two who
had had relations with thirty-five girls wrote, "I have to
have intercourse, as it has grown to be a habit." Another
wrote, "I see no reason for a normal man not to have
sexual intercourse if he knows how to care for himself."

Precocity

Although less mature mentally, the Hot-Bloods ran
far ahead of their fellows in a precocious haste to assume
the license and privileges of manhood. Impulsive, breezy
lads tending to have few fears or inhibitions, in temperament as well as in sexual behavior they were the anti-
thesis of the men who maintained their virginity. Even
before they reached adolescence, girls had begun to take
an important place in their lives. Whereas more than
half of the virgin group had not dated girls either in
high school or college, three-quarters of the Hot-Bloods
were not only dating, but were hot petting while still in
high school.

The most startling figures dealing with the men as revealed by this study concern the early age at which they
began their overt sexual experience. Of the 307 nonvirgin undergraduate men two-thirds had had their first
sexual intercourse while still in high school.

The Hot-Bloods carried this precocity to an extreme. Several told of attempting intercourse before they were ten. Others began their sexual adventures with the onset of adolescence at twelve to fourteen. Half of the Hot-Bloods had had their first sexual intercourse at sixteen or earlier, whereas only 15 per cent of the Moderates had been initiated by the time they were sixteen. Half of this group had their first intercourse with a girl of their own class, one-third went to prostitutes for their first experience, and about 15 per cent were initiated by older women.

Sexual precocity and promiscuity usually went together. Three-quarters of the group who began at fourteen or under were Hot-Bloods. A number of the precocious were included among the dozen who had had the highest number of affairs recorded in the study, claiming twenty to fifty girls each.

On First Acquaintance

The precocious, promiscuous boys were almost uniformly impulsive. They were adepts in the whirlwind courtship technique. Exclusive of those initiated by prostitutes, 10 per cent of the group had known their first sexual partner less than a week. One affair was reported to have occurred thirty minutes after meeting, others within a few hours. Several boys had intercourse with girls of their own class whom they had met that day or evening.

It is possible that the brevity of the acquaintance was for some men an essential part of its charm. A lad of seventeen who conquered his first girl in thirty minutes found this strange girl the more attractive because she had no associations with his little-boy past. She could accept him for the masterful male that he was just discovering himself to be.

Characteristically, the men as well as the women were reluctant to admit that the other person had taken the lead in ending the intimacy. About one-quarter of all affairs reported by the Hot-Bloods broke off immediately because of distances involved. These included chance meetings on vacations, visits, house parties. For the rest, the Hot-Bloods avoided admitting, even to themselves, no doubt, that the girl had tired first. As one man put it with unconscious humor, "She cared for another boy— and I let him have her."

Reasons given for breaking off were packed with significance and suggest plots for short-short stories in single phrases. The commonest reason was different versions of "I got tired of her." Individual comments were: "She was too damned homely," "I broke off after she was married," "She had an abortion," and in one case where the boy gave no further details, "She had a child."

Crude Youth

Youth and especially the young male, can be very cruel. He may be merely thoughtless, or he may have an imperious young ego that demands attention. The Hot-Bloods included the largest proportion of crude, lusty young animals for whom sex is sex and no frills about it. More characteristically than the other types, the Hot-Bloods were motivated by the hunter's instinct. One student considered it a chief disadvantage of the prostitute that "she affords no thrill of conquest." Another, describing the type of girl he liked to date, wrote, "She must be at least a little hard to get—but gettable." If no attractive girl of his own class is available, a man of this type finds himself a prostitute. They told their stories with ingenuous crudity: boy wants girl, boy finds girl, boy takes girl.

A man of twenty-one attending a metropolitan university described his first affair at seventeen with a girl of his own class. It was in her bedroom one evening when her family were out. "I seduced her after working on her for a year." It did not usually take so long. "She was a high type girl, very nice parents. . . . I induced her to try it after going steady with her about ninety days." Another man wrote of "a well-educated, intelligent girl, a virgin." "I got her emotionally aroused and keen for intercourse by caressing her."

The son of a Pacific coast businessman had his first affair when he was seventeen. It was one evening after rehearsal for a high-school play and he was taking her home in his father's car. She was "a nice type of girl," he wrote, and afterwards "she cried for a spell." Their affair continued for a year and a half until he left home to go to college, but he looked back on it with indifference and said that it had not made him care any more for the girl, even at the time.

The Irresponsibles

When a man is twenty-one it is not enough to be whimsical and impulsive. There is a fascination about sheer recklessness. This irresponsibility is a youthful characteristic especially exasperating to older people, but it is an integral part of being young. And why not? they ask. Why should youth be cautious and long-sighted? Time enough for that later. So they crowd each other down the primrose path. "Personally I would just like to have a good thorough fling before I settle down." "When do I want to marry? After I get through sowing my wild oats." "Marriage? As far off as possible. I suppose I'll fall for it, but I shan't until I have to."

By their own accounts they were rarely called upon to pay the piper, which suggests that they may have exaggerated their recklessness. This, too, would be part of their pattern. About 70 per cent of the Hot-Bloods had picked up birth-control information while still in high school, "enough to protect the girl"; "had sense enough to be careful." Nearly all recalled other boys' high-school affairs which ran on the rocks, resulting in abortions and forced marriages.

The Hot-Bloods' impulsive methods and hasty courtships more than neutralized their advantages in the way of greater information, and they reported over twice as many abortions in their own experience as did the Moderates. Ten per cent admitted having caused the pregnancy of one or more girls. Most of the girls had abortions by operation. In a few cases the men wrote vaguely of medicinal abortifacients.

Gossip and popular fiction have built up the notion of dissolute goings-on among the younger generation. In view of the students' evident frankness in both questionnaires and interviews, we heard of surprisingly few adventures that even bordered on orgies. A nineteen-year-old son of a Western mechanic wrote vaguely of a girl who had been made ill by having intercourse with three or four men in succession. A few described their first experience as having been semipublic, in one case a high-school initiation, in another a drunken party. One of the Western students interviewed in the East told of an orgy among high-school students that caused a town scandal. In the end the affair was allowed to drop as sons and daughters of the town's most prominent citizens were involved.

Liquor and Sex

Although this study contradicted traditional notions about city and country boys, it tended to confirm another old-fashioned idea about the relationship between liquor and sex. More than half of the Hot-Bloods as compared with only 15 per cent of the Uninitiated had begun to drink while in high school. By the time they reached college, more than 90 per cent of the Hot-Bloods were drinking and only 50 per cent of the Uninitiated.

Not all the men admitted that liquor served as an aphrodisiac in their own cases. Many denied it, or discounted the effect. One highly promiscuous man wrote, "I have occasionally slept with a girl after drinking whom I might not otherwise have slept with, but I remember no such affair which lasted beyond the evening or possibly the week end."

In a general way the findings of this study check with a recent survey of the drinking habits of the young men and women of New York State between eighteen and twenty-five years old. This survey, made by Dr. Paul Studenski of New York University under the auspices of Mrs. John S. Sheppard, committee chairman of the National Conference of State Liquor Administrators, was based on more than 2,000 questionnaires, a majority of them received from the college men and women of New York City. The questionnaires reported 87 per cent of drinkers, which corresponds to the 85 per cent of men drinkers among the nonvirgin group of our study, but not to the 68 per cent of drinkers for our total group of men. It was to be expected that Dr. Studenski's survey, confined largely to metropolitan colleges, would show a higher proportion of drinkers of both sexes than ours, since our students represent a cross section for the whole country.

A careful estimate of student drinking during prohibition days comes very near to these averages. It suggests that drinking is somewhat a matter of self-expression and that the men who are going to drink will drink regardless of efforts to enforce laws on the subject. James Anderson Hawes, traveling secretary of the Delta Kappa Epsilon fraternity for the last twenty years, writing during the latter years of prohibition—1929—estimated that at least 80 per cent of the American student body sometimes drank some form of liquor.

Like the men in our own study, the men contributing to Dr. Studenski's survey were divided in their opinions as to the relation of liquor and sex. A slight majority of the younger students, eighteen to twenty-one, reported no relation between drinking and sex. A slight majority of the older students, twenty-one to twenty-five, thought it caused a considerable loss of restraint. A majority of the nondrinking students considered that liquor served as a sexual release for others.

A majority of the men in our study failed to answer the questions in the schedules on the relationship of liquor and sex, suggesting that they had not made up their minds on the subject. Of those who did answer in the nonvirgin group, 60 per cent thought liquor had not "been responsible for the beginning of affairs," while 40 per cent thought that it had. Variation between groups corresponded to their sexual habits. The Hot-Bloods divided about half and half. Of the Discriminating men three-quarters thought liquor had not affected their sexual adventures.

Somewhat similar conclusions were reached by Peck and Wells in their survey of the psychosexuality of a group of 180 men graduates during the 1920's. Nearly half the men failed to answer a question as to the influence of liquor. Eleven per cent thought it exerted an influence, 44 that it did not. Peck and Wells concluded that the scholarly sounding adage "Sine Cerere et Baccho fuget Venus" was not borne out by the findings.

As a check on students' opinions that liquor had played little part in their own sexual intimacies, it is interesting to find that these same students were agreed upon its importance in the affairs of other men. Two-thirds of the Hot-Bloods, including many who were themselves drinkers, quoted instances in which drinking had precipitated sexual affairs among their friends.

This discrepancy suggests a possible defensiveness on the students' part. Man has always been sensitive to fancied reflections upon his potency. In all sincerity he repudiates anything which detracts from his virility. In support of their observation of the effects of liquor on friends and classmates, the Hot-Bloods cited many specific cases. The son of a scientist from a small town in New England, attending a university in another small town, wrote in reference to five abortions, "Four of these cases occurred when both parties were intoxicated and did not take any precautions until too late. A girl can easily take care of herself if she knows how." He added, "If a girl is influenced by drink, she is not in her right mind and should not be touched; it should be regarded in the light of rape."

Most of the Hot-Bloods were less punctilious about the girl who had been drinking. Characteristic phrases were: "A girl is easier to make if she is tight"; "girls who go the limit are generally drunk"; "we were both stewed and didn't bother about any birth control—fortunately nothing happened"; "an alcoholic glow is a great help all round." This ruthlessness is—with individual excep-

tions—typical of the Hot-Bloods' attitude. It is a mixture
of inexperience and selfishness. They are out for a good
time and the devil take the hindmost. Something of the
casual jocularity of the campus attitude toward drinking
is conveyed in the special vocabulary nicely defining the
successive stages of intoxication: high, tight, looping,
stinking, plastered, out.

Pick-ups

The use of alcohol to help along chance encounters
was general. "I couldn't pick up a girl if I weren't
drunk." "You can always pick up a town girl and take
her to a hotel, but you have to be fried to do it."

Stopping halfway between the girl of his own class and
the paid prostitute, the hunter type frequently seeks his
pleasure on city or small-town streets, in restaurants and
dance halls. In some colleges these pick-ups are known
as "townies." They may be girls who have jobs—wait-
resses, dance-hall hostesses, clerks in stores, telephone
girls, even nurses from the local hospital. Sometimes they
are girls living at home, looking for a good time. They
do not charge for their favors. In exchange for an evening's fun, perhaps dinner and a movie, or whatever the
town affords, they are willing to be taken to a furnished
room or to a hotel. If they do not live with their family,
they may take the man to their own room. Usually these
are one-night affairs.

The Hot-Bloods were especially cynical toward these
girls, showed no compunction about using them or about
the possibility of making them pregnant, and were contemptuous in their comments. They found no compan-
ionship with them and pursued them quite deliberately
for physical relief. This was especially true of the colleges
for men only where the students are isolated in a rather

monastic atmosphere during their college years. Some of the men in other groups do not mind it, but the Hot-Bloods become restless and eager for the society of the other sex. One student who had begun his experiences at the age of twelve and had had intimate affairs with fifteen to twenty-five girls, wrote: "At the end of any lengthy period of continence I find it difficult to be natural and friendly with a girl."

Young men meet this situation with a variety of devices. A few men—not many can afford it—may keep mistresses on various terms. A small group of three or four friends may rent a small apartment and install one or two girls for their exclusive use. These girls may have daytime jobs or they may be frankly prostitutes.

Prostitutes

Anomalous as is the position of the amateur light-o'-love there is a sharp corner to be turned between her and the commercialized prostitute. Several men who had patronized a prostitute for their first experience remarked parenthetically that first they got a little tight. Saturday night binges seemed to be fairly common. Almost twice as many Hot-Bloods as Moderates had had first affairs with prostitutes, including many of the young boys who began at fourteen and fifteen. "In a business-like way I went to a brothel"; "I picked up a strumpet on the streets of Paris"; "I wanted to find out what a house of prostitution was like"; "I am strongly sexed emotionally. I went to a professional for the first time to learn how to behave under a less mechanical sexual relief."

Of the two-thirds of the Hot-Bloods who began sex relations in high school, one-quarter went to houses of prostitution. For the group as a whole, including those who delayed initiation until they reached college, the proportion who sought prostitutes for first experience rose to one-third. Ten per cent of the group had never stayed with a prostitute and this included some of the men who had been most promiscuous with girls of their own class. A majority, both of those who had and those who had not made use of disorderly houses, condemned their use.

Practically all referred to danger of disease as the chief objection to the prostitute, including the men who had patronized them most liberally. Other disadvantages mentioned were: loss of self-respect, unsatisfied feeling, danger to reputation, sordidness. Now and then a vivid phrase suggested intensity of revulsion. A boy of seventeen who had had relations with eight girls, four of them prostitutes, wrote down as the disadvantage, "more soiled." Another wrote, "too sordid and mechanical"; A.H., aged nineteen, who had taken only girls of his own class, wrote, "danger of disease and violation of my own clean body." A.J., who had patronized forty prostitutes, wrote as disadvantages: "danger of disease and esthetic and again esthetic." A.K. wanted to discuss "why young men cannot have intercourse without resorting to prostitutes and shame." A few men—only three and all radicals —objected to prostitution on social grounds, having in mind the effect on the girl.

The 40 per cent of the Hot-Bloods who defended prostitution stressed the convenience and freedom from responsibility. They argued that the prostitute meets an urgent biological need and does not burden a man with fear of pregnancy or entanglements. They also considered it desirable to learn from an experienced person. Several approved the relationship as more convenient and businesslike. They accepted as an advantage the mechanical impersonality which repelled others.

A.K., a student at a major Eastern university, put the case for the brothel with clarity: "I think intercourse with prostitutes is highly advisable in the *first* few experiences. They overcome all self-consciousness on the part of the neophyte, make the incident a frank one, and are inclined to tear away the pernicious shroud of shame and mysticism which has enveloped it until that time. With experience I think most men of good moral taste are disinclined to make habitual use of prostitutes."

A.K., the son of a lawyer, was twenty-two years old. He had had intercourse with twelve girls of his own class and with about 24 prostitutes, not beginning until he was eighteen. He had tried the experiment of keeping a mistress—with no great satisfaction. He was a deliberate sort who filled out his questionnaire with meticulous neatness and knew how to spell the generally misspelled word condom. He was an unsentimental and calculating person on the alert for his own interests. It is a question whether his complacency or his intelligence will come out ahead, probably the former.

Quite a different type of man to argue in favor of the prostitute was A.L. The son of a salesman in the Far West, he attended a Pacific coast college. An exceptional type in this group, he was full of inhibitions. Although he had petted and dated "every available kind of girl" from high-school days on, he had never been in love. An outburst against the older generation suggested a surcharged emotional background. He thought it "ethically wrong for older folk to take advantage of the helplessness of the young by impressing upon them the deification of the cult of inhibition."

He first had intercourse at eighteen. In the three years since, he had had relations with thirteen girls, four of them prostitutes. He described his first experience with youthful literalness. He had gone to a prostitute. They had complete privacy, he said, "a room, a bed, a sink." He took the lead, but he was very nervous. He never saw the prostitute again, but he wrote of her, after three years, with pathetic gratitude:

"This prostitute happened to be a very sympathetic creature and was not coarse. She realized that I was not as calm as I might have been and told me that if I was to give future female partners the satisfaction they desired, I'd have to take it easy, getting control over myself. I knew all that already, but it served to quiet me down. All in all, it was a very satisfactory experience except that there was no opportunity for developing a more lasting relationship. The lady's profession obviously was a drawback."

It was probably a factor in this boy's situation that his parents' home life was unhappy and that he had never been able to discuss sexual matters with either of them. His baffled outburst against the "deification of the cult of inhibition," his gratitude to an anonymous and exceptional prostitute who was gentle and patient with him, leave a picture of groping bewilderment. It seems stupidly wasteful that, in spite of advances in child psychology and progressive education, society should have been unable to devise a more civilized method of preparing young men to enter manhood than to leave them to make the best of furtive encounters in brothels and to run the danger of venereal disease. An irresponsible Hot-Blood, half full of liquor, turned loose in a "house" is taking odds against himself that he would not consider in betting or in business. Actually only two Hot-Bloods, out of a total of five in the entire group of 243 experienced men, admitted having contracted venereal disease.

We have no way of knowing how many men failed to admit it.

Don Juans

The ultrapromiscuous type of man raises the old question of heredity *vs.* environment. How much is he the product of home, school, and background? Or is he born a hunter?

The psychoanalytic theory of the Don Juan type, the more than normally promiscuous man, is ironically prosaic. It helped perhaps to dissipate any glamour clinging to the legend of the archseducer. The Count de Casanova, announced Dr. Freud in effect, was merely an aggravated case of mamma's boy. He had never been able to wean himself from an infantile sense that his mother was a being of immeasurable wisdom and authority, of incomparable beauty and tenderness. She offered him unfailing understanding and protection in a perilous world.

None of the charming girls with whom he might fancy himself in love could survive comparison with this paragon, the mother of his imagination. So began a life-long search for an ideal. It was a quest foredoomed to failure and heartache both for himself and for the girls whom he would disappoint.

The theory offers an interesting background for speculation about the dozen Don Juans among the Hot-Bloods. Their questionnaires threw little light on its soundness, however. Such trends are deeply overlaid and not to be casually revealed.

The chief impression left by the Don Juans was of their immaturity. They were the playboy type who continue to be the life of their college reunions until the end of the chapter. They exaggerated qualities of the larger group as though seen through a magnifying glass. They seemed unaware of the disproportionate amount of time which they as students were devoting to girls and sex. They were too self-indulgent, too well armored in egotism, to be made uncomfortable by any such consciousness. They were direct, uncomplicated lads, not intellectual, not given to puzzling about anything. As one wrote, "I like things simple." Sex for them was mainly, if not exclusively, a physical function. They were unaware of its subtleties.

Four of the Don Juans had lawyer fathers. The others were sons of bankers, scientists, a clergyman, and a merchant. Half of them planned to follow the same occupation as their fathers—a much higher proportion than obtained for the other Hot-Bloods. Content to follow in their fathers' footsteps, they evidently were not a rebellious group. Their excessive indulgence in sex was not part of a general defiance of home standards.

A possible interpretation in terms of economic determinism might be supported by the fact that half of the Hot-Bloods had attended private school as compared with an average of one-quarter for all the men. Their ultrapromiscuity may have developed parasitelike from a youth marked by too much money, opportunity, and pleasure, plus that certain arrogant irresponsibility characteristic of the privileged child. Against this theory it is equally true that the boys of the privileged group conformed to no one pattern. Some of them were most circumspect.

The son of a Middle Western banker was fairly typical of the Don Juans. After preparing at a famous Eastern private school, he was, at twenty-one, a student at a coeducational state university. His first affair, at fifteen, had been with an older woman, "a divorcee of good type," whom he had known for two hours. It ended when she, a visitor, left the city within a few days.

He claimed he had had sexual relations with forty to fifty girls and with ten prostitutes; thought he had been in love three times. He realized that drinking had precipitated many of his own and his friends' affairs. He considered continence "stupid" and said he hunted up a girl whenever he felt desire. He would not demand virginity of his wife, might marry a promiscuous girl, "depending on the girl," and, for all his extensive experience, was not sure whether or not he would be willing to initiate a virgin. He would hope for fidelity from his wife, but was not at all sure that he would be able to give it.

His views about women contradicted his behavior; he took a fairly advanced theoretical position, whereas his conduct implied the old-fashioned love-'em-and-leave-'em attitude. He was a typical playboy. Having had more than ordinary advantages, he was a pleasant person, conventional, self-centered, quite undistinctive. There was not one item about his questionnaire that made him stand out except the number of his affairs and his two-hour first courtship.

Some Don Juans used phrases which suggested an awakening sense that sex, in spite of its irresistible allure, would always bring disillusionment. One lad who, at eighteen, could not remember how many girls he had had, recommended going to a prostitute because "she reveals the futility of the sexual act." A Southern student agreed "with Huxley that sex is much overrated." Another disapproved college marriages because the boy and girl "would get so tired of each other."

Attitude Toward Women

The Hot-Bloods sorted themselves out of the group of
undergraduates by their behavior. They were the men
who had been the most promiscuous. Fully as significant
as the roll call of their physical conquests was their
mental and emotional attitude toward women.

One practical measure of this attitude may be found
in their recognition of their share of responsibility for
the outcome of their amours. Almost two-thirds of the
Hot-Bloods failed to answer a question as to whether
any of their girls had become pregnant. Men who answered practically every other question left this blank.
Only twelve Hot-Bloods admitted that they had impreg-
nated girls. In reply to the theoretic question as to what
they would do in case of a girl's pregnancy, only one-
third of the Hot-Bloods thought that they should marry
the girl as compared with 47 per cent of all the experienced men of the study. A larger number thought that
they should help her arrange for an abortion, and only
ten of the entire group, eight of them Hot-Bloods, said
that they would leave the girl to work matters out for
herself as best she might. Six of the eight were obviously
neurotic.

What Care I How Chaste She Be?

Sir Walter Raleigh wrote these words in the sixteenth
century but they were only a rhetorical question and
meant that he cared very much. The modern young
man's literal acceptance of this sentiment would have
been unthinkable. . . .

Young men still find infinite provocation and glamour
in pursuit of the not impossible she. But the basic attitude toward woman has become amazingly unromantic

and practical. As Dean Gauss of Princeton has put it, "all those secondary psychological traits which once differentiated men and women, placed them in two different worlds, have ceased to exist and life has been reduced to a common denominator for both."

With striking unanimity young men today paraphrase Sir Walter's rhetorical question. Of the Hot-Bloods 90 per cent stated that they would not strongly insist on marrying a virgin. Nearly a quarter said that they would prefer not to marry a virgin and another quarter said that a girl's virginity was a matter of complete indifference: "irrelevant"; "other considerations of greater importance"; "depends entirely on the girl and whether I love her."

The complementary question as to their willingness to initiate a virgin revealed one of the typical conflicts between old and new codes which snarl up transition periods. Only 30 per cent carried it off consistently and said that they had no hesitation. This minority included the men already quoted who referred with a certain swagger to their experience in seducing virgins. Some of the phrases used by the 70 per cent who avowed their hesitation suggested an atavistic chivalry of which they may scarcely have been aware.

The nineteen-year-old son of a Middle Western minor executive was a matter-of-fact young man, planning to go into business. He had never been in love and had had relations with eight or ten girls but no prostitutes. He would not insist upon marrying a virgin, but when it came to initiating one he had strong scruples. Emphatically, he would never deflower a virgin and considered it "the dirtiest trick any man can do."

"Of course I would hesitate," wrote a New Yorker. "I don't want to be first until I marry." Sometimes they mix

the chivalry with cynicism. "Virgins are apt to be rather
a nuisance," wrote one man speaking from experience.
"If I could find a virgin," wrote another, "I'd rather not
have intercourse with her if there was a chance that she'd
regret her loss." Another man drew a distinction: he
would hesitate with the girl of fourteen but not with
seventeen.

Describing the kind of girl they liked to date, only one-
fifth of the Hot-Bloods specified that they preferred "the
girl who won't." Four-fifths of the group were evenly
divided between indifference and a frank preference for
"the girl who will," in characteristic contrast to the inexperienced boys, two-thirds of whom preferred to date
"the girl who won't," despite the fact that three-quarters
of the latter group said they would not insist on marrying a virgin.

On the question of willingness to marry a girl who had
been promiscuous, the Hot-Bloods divided half and half.
Several queried the use of the word promiscuous or suggested qualified definitions. The son of a Middle Western
professional man wrote, "The promiscuous girl is one
who has intercourse with nearly everyone who tries to
make her. A girl may have had intercourse with a number of men without being called promiscuous." Another
man wrote, analytically, "The promiscuous girl is O.K.
if she maintains a balance in her own mind." And another, "Insist on marrying a virgin? It depends on how
she is not a virgin. Am against whores."

The Double Standard

A small minority of these promiscuous lads were as
intolerant of girls who enjoy their freedom as the most
priggish virgin: "I have nothing to do with promiscuous
girls"; "I despise them"; "contempt and pity." The son

of a Southern physician who stated that he had had relations with forty girls coolly asserted that the promiscuous girl was "a danger and should be shunned."

These intolerant young men, although they might indignantly deny it, were quite behind the times. They had picked up and were carrying on the timeworn tradition of the double standard. They had two codes, one for the marriageable girl, another for the "easy make." The prostitute was taken for granted. They might report having had intercourse with a total of five or six girls. Further down the page they might refer to ten or twenty prostitutes who apparently did not count.

The double-standard man demanded virginity of the girl he married. His own record was irrelevant. There were a few exceptions. An artist who had had a dozen intimate affairs and insisted on marrying a virgin added apologetically, "I realize how selfish it is on my part, but I feel that 90 per cent of men will demand the same." A young scientist who claimed he had had affairs with thirty to thirty-five girls said he did not feel that he could insist on a girl's virginity. "I would prefer to, but believe there should be no double standard of morality."

It is in character that the Hot-Bloods leaned more heavily toward the double standard than the other groups, though even with them it was favored by only 10 per cent. It remains to be seen whether the 90 per cent will be able to live up to their declaration. Indifferent to virginity in the abstract, they may discover, as they approach marriage, that it becomes more important than they had anticipated.

Men have behind them a long tradition of demanding virginity and fidelity of their women. They have enforced it with every form of pressure: social ostracism, legal codes, punishments, torture, and death. The student of social customs may find a connection between this sudden tolerance and the rapidly increasing economic independence of women. Through the centuries when women had no means of livelihood except as wives or widows or courtesans, men could demand pretty much what they pleased and had the means to enforce their demands. Economic emancipation of women during recent generations has changed the picture. With a facility in itself impressive the younger generation of both sexes are swiftly adapting themselves to the changed conditions.

No generalizations about 100 men or ten or even two will always apply, for each man is a law unto himself and in one thing or another as individual as his own thumbprint. All the strange network of emotional drives and inhibitions which have crisscrossed through him since infancy turn him out, obstinately unyielding on one point, whimsically susceptible on another.

Not all the Hot-Bloods were matter-of-fact or egotistical lads. Some were warmhearted and sensitive. And always they presented inconsistency and paradox. A.P. had his first affair at seventeen with a girl five years his senior. Looking back at twenty-one, he wrote that he had broken off the affair after a few weeks "because she was too sexy." Yet in the four years since he had had intercourse with fifteen other girls.

Descriptions of their first affairs were sometimes youthfully ecstatic. "I was alone with a newly-married woman only a little older than I—nineteen—in her apartment. She was charming and sophisticated." The most romantic memories lingered around affairs consummated on summer evenings in deserted countrysides, "late at night in an open field under the stars"; "on a deserted shore under the trees."

A Middle Western boy of twenty-one wrote of sex experience, "there is a beauty and satisfaction, a feeling of self." A Southerner commented that his relationships with girls "made me aware of dark depths inside me." A hard-boiled lad of varied experience wrote that his affairs had made him "feel the beauty of a woman's body." A young artist wrote of love, "Sometimes it is a bond, sometimes a torch."

Composite Pattern

A composite picture of the Hot-Bloods would be full of paradox. Popular predisposition is all in favor of the impulsive boy who rushes headlong, "risks all, nor counts the cost." Romantic fiction and the movies, both of which build heroes on the principle of giving the consumer some one with whom he enjoys identifying himself, used to favor the impulsive character reformed by love. In recent years, with the relaxation of our moral codes, less space is given to reform. Plots have been increasingly picaresque. The hero is the same, the breezy, irresponsible big-boy with heart of gold.

Realistic analysis of the individual record leaves a less glamorous impression than the fantasies of Hollywood and the pulp writers. The Hot-Bloods' lives center too exclusively round their ego for social comfort. Self-indulgence is too often all that matters. It is part of the impulsive and irresponsible Hot-Blood pattern to refuse either to look ahead or to look back. He will neither be forewarned nor profit by his mistakes.

Personally he is often one of the most popular men on the campus. Versatile, enthusiastic, he is free from the fears and inhibitions which slow up some of the men in other groups. If he could only grasp in time the necessity of getting himself under control, he could have the world in his sling.

Gilbert Chesterton said that there was nothing so important to a man's landlady as his philosophy of life. In some such rudimentary terms, it does not seem too much to expect of the college man as a by-product of the discipline of four years of academic training, that he shall work out for himself a philosophy, or at least some elementary formulation of the values he wants from life. Capacity for discrimination is the test of civilization. . . .

4.
Impotence and Frigidity

by Karl A. Menninger, M. D.

One of America's leading psychiatrists, Dr. Menninger is perhaps best known for the work carried on at the famous Midwestern clinic that bears the family name. Here, he considers two of the most prevalent functional disorders of men and women. Impotence and frigidity are seen as symptoms of unconscious conflict in which the desire for pleasure is circumvented by other factors in the personality. Reprinted from *Man Against Himself* by Karl A. Menninger, M.D., copyright, 1938, by Karl A. Menninger, by permission of Harcourt, Brace & Company. See also Chapter 4 in Women: "Potency and Receptivity."

ONE OF THE RESULTS of the scientific exploration of the unconscious mental life was the recognition of something which no child, no savage, no animal, and no simple, honest natural man needs to be told—namely, the importance to the individual of his genital organs and his sexual life. It seems strange now that for Freud to have pointed out this obvious fact and the way in which civilization tended to obscure and deny it hypocritically, should have called forth upon him such a torrent of abuse from all quarters, abuse which only branded its authors as ignorant, hypocritical, or neurotic. Nevertheless, it is still possible to discover traces of this formerly prevalent prudery.

Take, for example, the general attitude toward the functional impairment, functional *destruction*, of genitality, i.e., sexual impotence and sexual frigidity. So widespread are these affections in some degree or other as to be regarded by some authorities as almost universal among "civilized" peoples, an inevitable sacrifice to the advance of civilization.[1] In the face of this, it is an eloquent testimony to the persistence of the Victorian (and earlier) hypocrisy that even in scientific circles this subject is still taboo. To write or speak of it is almost to label oneself a charlatan or a sensationalist. A leading standard textbook of medicine, for example, refers to impotence in only three places and to frigidity nowhere; references to the impairment of walking, on the other hand, occupy in the same book more than a *full page of the index*!

The bookstores are flooded with well meant and well constructed treatises on sex and many of them are quite explicit about those serious and widespread afflictions, gonorrhea and syphilis. Impotence and frigidity are far more prevalent and, from the patient's point of view, more serious.

Impotence as a transitory symptom is an almost universal experience—although it is often denied. Habitual impotence, partial or complete, is much more frequent than is generally known or assumed, even by physicians. Some men are constantly humiliated or depressed about it, while others accept it philosophically as something inexplicable but irremediable. Some actually do not realize their own condition. Many men who believe themselves to be potent and who perform the sexual act in a mechanically correct way, often to the complete satisfaction of their wives, obtain from it only a minimum of pleasure; this absence of pleasure is an unrecognized form of impotence. Another manifestation of this same kind of psychic impotence is a feeling of regret and

[1] See Freud, S.: *Collected Papers,* Vol. IV, *Contributions to the Psychology of Love,* pp. 192-235; and *Civilization and Its Discontents,* New York, Jonathan Cape and Harrison Smith, 1930, p. 76.

loss after the completion of the act. I recall one patient, for example, who, having insisted upon the intercourse would, upon its completion, reproach his wife bitterly for having permitted him to perform it, declaring that now he would be nervous and exhausted all day, might catch cold, and might be weakened mentally. Still another form of impotence, frequently not recognized as such, consists in a prematurity of orgasm.

It may not be self-evident that frigidity in women is identical, psychologically, with impotence in men. Certainly in the popular mind they are not the same; impotence is assumed to be exceptional and frigidity to be frequent but less serious. Numerous statistical investigations as to the frequency of frigidity in women have been made, but no one thinks of making such an inquiry among men. This is partly due to the more subtle forms which male impotence so often takes, but even more, I think, to the tacit approval of sexual repression in women. There are actually people of both sexes who do not know that conscious sexual feeling is ever experienced by women.

A total uninterest in genital sexuality, a tolerance of intercourse "for my husband's sake," a complete lack of feeling, either painful or pleasurable, characterize a very large number of women, if clinical experience and statistical inquiries are to be given any reliance. Women so afflicted frequently show some intellectual interest in sex, may even read books on the subject, but as a rule, like their male counterparts, do not consult physicians, do not discuss it with friends or neighbors. The whole subject is a closed book, to be mentioned as little as possible.

In sharp contrast to the preceding group in this respect are those women who have faint or inconstant feelings of pleasure connected with intercourse and even—at long

intervals—an occasional orgasm. These women are, as a
rule, genuinely concerned over their affliction and make
energetic efforts to become normal. They read books on
the subject in great numbers; they consult friends, neighbors, doctors, and quacks; they try all sorts of experi-
ments. I recall a man and wife who had been so distressed over the wife's frigidity that they had even tried
the experiment of having a friend of the husband cohabit
with the wife to see if this might "make a difference."
Probably many instances of marital unfaithfulness in
women depend in part upon this motive.

These conditions—both in men and in women—have
been interpreted in many ways. Occasionally (rarely)
structural, "organic" changes have been found and caus-
ality ascribed to them; operations without number and
(in my opinion) without rationale have been performed;
glandular theories have been evolved and appropriate
treatments devised to fit these theories, and all of these
have—occasionally—had therapeutic success. But so have
hypnotism and snake oil; it is trite but necessary to add
that occasional therapeutic success proves nothing.

All these theories of structural and chemical etiology
are correct, but they are not true. They are *part* of the
truth; but they ignore the psychological factor. Physical
factors (structural changes) do contribute to the pathology; chemical factors (glandular misfunctioning) do
contribute also; but psychological factors also contribute,
and (in my opinion)—*in this particular affliction*—are
more accessible to view, more amenable to change, and
more responsive to therapy, in the average case, than the
physical and chemical factors.

We can consider such functional impairment as an
inhibition, a negative symptom as it were, and, in a
sense, a loss or *destruction* of normal activity, normal

pleasure. It is the functional equivalent of actual self-castration, in that the genitals, while not sacrificed in substance, are treated as if nonexistent. And just as self-castration is the prototype of all self-mutilation, so impotence is the prototype of all functional inhibitions. In this sense it might be said to constitute the original pattern and exemplification of hysteria. The characteristic feature of hysteria is this surrendering of a function in lieu of surrender of the organ itself.

When we speak of a symptom as hysterical in its origin, what we mean is that it has arisen through modifications in form or function of an organ to satisfy certain unconscious purposes and intentions of the personality. We know that all functions of the organism strive to carry out the wishes, the instinctive cravings, of the individual in the face of a hostile or indifferent environment. The physiologists have demonstrated that when danger threatens and we wish to fight, the body automatically prepares itself. Blood rushes *from* the skin and *to* the muscles, glycogen is mobilized in large quantities, adrenalin and prothrombin are poured out to expedite physiological defense. All of this is accomplished automatically by the body to make possible the fulfillment of pugnacious wishes, wishes which may be scarcely conscious.

These defense reactions may involve more complex units. For example, a soldier in the trenches is "shell-shocked." Paralyzed with fright, his legs conveniently refuse to carry him into the field of greater danger. These extended defense reactions are not discriminatory and not so automatically self-regulating as the older and simpler ones, and so such a man's legs also refuse to carry him anywhere else, even to a place of greater safety. Thus we recognize that such defenses, although carrying out the purposes of one wish, violate other wishes of the personality—and hence we call them symptoms. Symptoms are, in a sense, always destructive and when they arise in this way they may be fairly described as products of self-destructive combinations. This is true, even though the determining "wish" or impulse leading to the conflict and the symptom is self-preservative. The soldier sacrifices (for a time) the use of his legs in order to save (as he thinks) his life. Self-preservation wins, but at the cost of a minor (at least a lesser) self-destruction.

The fact that the conflict is unconscious is intrinsic in the explanation. A *conscious* wish can be dealt with rationally—either gratified or denied and the solution accepted. But unconscious wishes (including fears from which we wish to escape) are dealt with in unconscious automatic ways, often exceedingly irrational and unpropitious for the personality, by symptoms and inhibitions. Back of these is always an unconscious wish and a conflict.

Impotence and frigidity may be regarded as strictly comparable with an hysterical paralysis of the leg from shell shock. We must ask ourselves what in the normal act of reproduction can assume for so many people the terror and danger of a battlefield, so much so as to induce the voluntary surrender ("self-destruction") of the power and pleasure of the act? What great and irrational fear can be harbored in the unconscious to make necessary this automatic defense reaction in the face of such powerful conscious wishes to the contrary? We must expect great difficulty in ascertaining this because the functions of the sexual organs excite the highest degree of pride and shame; they are, therefore, veiled most obscurely.

The practicing physician's first thought would be what

some of his women patients have told him. "I want very much to let myself go," one says, "but I'm so afraid of pregnancy." Or perhaps she says because she is so afraid of being hurt by her husband. Men patients also complain that they cannot be potent with their wives for fear they may hurt them and are too much afraid of venereal disease to be potent with anyone else.

But we must not take these *conscious* fears too literally. Of course, they may be partly justified by reality, but only partly so. There are ways of circumventing pain, there are ways of avoiding venereal disease, there are ways of precluding pregnancy. We know from experience that such conscious fears are only "alibis." Beneath them are unconscious fears of great power, fears arising from various sources. We shall study them genetically in a special situation, a situation we regard as psychologically fundamental.

The Fear of Punishment

One of the most powerful determinants of unconscious fear is the expectation of punishment. In normal adults a distinction is made between things which society really does punish and acts for which one expects punishment only because of a childhood misapprehension. For many people sex is still a kind of evil-doing, hence punishable.

A man married to a woman who unconsciously represents to him a new edition of the mother who successfully inhibited his sexual activities during boyhood, could not possibly overcome this fear sufficiently to permit his body to act out his instinctive desires. . . .

One is unconsciously dominated by childhood attitudes throughout life. In the normal person, the unfortunate misunderstandings of childhood are corrected by later experience but it implies no weakness of intelligence that some persons cannot overcome them. The reactions of conscience are determined in early life and change but little as a result of experience. Accordingly, with or without the presence of conscious fears and quite independent of them, there exists in the unconscious of many people a compelling fear of punishment which is excited to great activity at the very moment when the ego believes itself threatened with an alluring temptation of a nature once associated with punitive pain, and the prohibition of this pleasure is, at the same time, a punishment in itself.

All manner of devices are utilized by the unconscious to circumvent this fear and to permit the forbidden sexual indulgences to be psychologically acceptable. For example, I recall a woman who could not enjoy intercourse with her husband because during the act a picture of her father with a stern, disapproving expression on his face would always appear before her. This woman and her husband had themselves discovered that if her husband would first strike her as if in anger she could then enjoy sexual intercourse normally. It is quite clear, I think, that this woman had the feeling so many children do that punishment squares everything, and one punishment will do as well (or better) than another. Therefore she could dispel this frowning face of her father by carrying out the punishment which she felt she deserved for indulging in an act of sex which he disapproved.

Precisely the same thing holds true of men. Indeed it is this need for punishment which explains the favorable results sometimes obtained by painful treatment administered to the genital organs by urologists and gynecologists, in spite of the fact that rarely, if ever, is either impotence or frigidity dependent upon structural pathology, endocrinopathic and neurologic cases excepted.

I shall repeat what was said above: *hysteria,* of which impotence and frigidity are typical, indeed prototypical, is definable as a condition in which the function of an organ is surrendered or modified—the purpose being the forestalling of anticipated injury to or removal of that organ. Put into more familiar terms, the hysterical organ invites (wishes for) punishment of a lesser order to avoid punishment of a greater order.

The Aggressive Component

Back of such expectation of punishment may lie only these childhood misconceptions and false associations. But clinical experience has shown that these are apt to be fused with less innocent elements. A common fear back of impotence and frigidity—sometimes conscious, more often unconscious—and common to both men and women, is the fear of injury to or being injured by the sexual partner. Such fears betray sadistic fantasies. We know that back of much that passes for love there is deep unconscious hatred, hatred that denies the erotic satisfaction one consciously seeks and at the same time, by means of this very self-denial, expresses the aggression— the hatred, rejection, contempt for the partner. This is particularly clear in the condition known as *ejaculatio praecox* where the man actually soils the woman, in addition to thwarting her, like an angry baby who wets his nurse.[2]

But why should a man hate a woman whom he thinks he loves? There are three common reasons for this:

[2]This condition was studied and the psychological factors analyzed in a masterful article by Abraham (Abraham, Karl: *Selected Papers on Psychoanalysis,* English translation by Bryan and Strachey, London, Hogarth Press, 1927, pp. 280-298).

One of the commonest bases for unconscious hate is the wish for revenge. This may be revenge for something that has recently happened or something that has happened long ago at the hands of an entirely different person. Many people go through life trying to take out on someone feelings that were generated within them as children. One recalls that Don Juan, the world's great cad, was deserted by his mother in early childhood; he spent his entire life treating other women in exactly the way that his mother treated him, first making them love him and then leaving them.

A male patient, a very successful man, was under psychoanalytic treatment on account of periodic depressions. In the course of treatment it developed that he manifested a certain kind of impotence with his wife. His erotic overtures were accompanied by tenderness and love which would greatly arouse his wife, whereupon he would either lose all interest or suffer *ejaculatio praecox*. In his analysis it became quite clear that the purpose of this was to thwart his wife, and in this it was indeed very successful. Intuitively she perceived the hostile nature of this abortive treatment and would become hysterically nervous and so distressed that she would cry and strike him with her fists. This would cause him to be remorseful and depressed. As a child this man had been raised in a family presided over by a very capable, energetic mother who was much more interested in her clubs and social activities than in her children. The patient had been the first born and was probably unplanned for because he interrupted a project which his mother had gotten under way and to which she devoted herself for a number of years after his birth, leaving him largely in the hands of a governess. During his analysis he remembered with great emotion how bitterly he had resented his mother's frequent desertion of him which even as a child he had protested against by fierce crying and what were called temper tantrums. When he was punished for these he only grew more resentful. He was thwarted by his mother and the wish to thwart her in return he had carried throughout his life.

Another reason for unconscious hate, especially on the part of women, is a wish not so much to get revenge for themselves as to avenge their mothers. They think as children that their mothers are suffering at the hands of their fathers and when they learn something of sexual intercourse they interpret it as a violent act of cruelty. Of course many women actually favor this impression on the part of their daughters, setting them against their own fathers and warning them that all men are to be feared. Such mothers think they are safeguarding their daughters, but we know they are also revenging themselves on their husbands. For these various reasons the daughter grows up determined to pay back this old grudge against the male. She masks this spirit of vengeance with love but sooner or later her husband feels the consequences.

A third reason for hate is envy. Unconsciously men envy women and women envy men to an extent far beyond ordinary recognition. To play the normal passive feminine role seems to some women a kind of humiliation which they cannot bear. In the presence of the hate dictated by such envy a woman cannot be other than frigid. Some men, on the other hand, often begrudge women not only their protected status and their social privileges, but (more fundamentally) their ability to bear children. This unconscious rejection of their biological role by men may be compensated for by their developing some other type of creativeness, but in other instances it betrays itself in direct but disguised manifestations of hate and envy of women on this basis.

I have in mind a patient, a successful, popular and apparently very normal man who underwent a long treatment at the hands of several competent physicians on account of one symptom, namely, the development of terrific anxiety wherever additional family responsibilities devolved upon him. Chief among these was the wish of his wife for some children. Intellectually he concurred in her wish but the contemplation of such a plan threw him into such distress that he had to resign his position and seemed to some of his physicians to be on the verge of a complete mental collapse. Another similar instance was a man who was a nationally known figure in the world of finance but, in his own home, a most pitiful object; his wife had begged him to give her a child but so frightened would he become at such a prospect that in spite of intense sexual desire and great emotional conflict he would discontinue all relations with her for months on end rather than run the "risk." The situation became so acute that his wife divorced him. He married another woman who became pregnant by him but before this child was born the man died!

Conflicting Loves

But fear and hate are not the only things which produce impotence and frigidity. The desire may be inhibited instead by conflicting erotic aims which decrease the available erotic energy. To put it very simply, a man may be impotent with a woman because he loves someone else and doesn't know it. The person loved may have lived long ago, may have been a childhood ideal such as in the case of the boy who is prevented from loving his wife because he is "tied to his mother's apron strings," and cannot love any other woman. Many men who marry are nevertheless so attached to their own mothers deep in their unconscious that they cannot give to their wives anything but the childlike love which a boy gives to his mother. In the sense that she is a wife, a sexual partner, such men cannot really accept her or treat her as she craves to be treated, providing, of course, that she, herself, is normal. Frequently one sees such mother-attached men falling in love with women who want to be mothers. Such unions may be fairly satisfactory; they cannot, however, be regarded as normal sexual unions, and many of them go upon the rocks.

Precisely the same sort of fixation occurs in the lives of many women. A girl may be so much in love with her own father that she cannot possibly accept a husband sexually. She may go through the motions of living with him, of loving him, and of cohabiting with him, but however well she may fool him—indeed, however well she may fool herself—she cannot enlist the services of her unconscious in this deception. The body cannot respond to a love situation which all her repressed feelings regard as disloyal to her first and real love.

There is another kind of conflicting love which is not so easily recognized as the fixation on the parents or a brother or a sister but which is almost as frequent. We know that in the process of transferring the affection which he first concentrated upon the father and mother to other persons outside the family the child goes through a stage in which he prefers persons of the same sex as himself. This *homosexual phase* in the course of the individual's development is ultimately repressed and represented only in the sublimated form in normal persons as the basis of much of the friendly intercourse of later life. In many individuals, however, either because it is excessive in quantity or because it has been favored or nurtured in some way, this homosexual element does not disappear. Such persons remain strongly but unconsciously attached to homosexual love objects, even though consciously they think they are normal heterosexual individuals. In fact it is just those unconsciously homosexual people who go about the world with Leporello[3] lists proving how heterosexually potent they are, as if to deny the secret which their unconscious whispers to them.

Finally there is a conflicting love which is more powerful than any of these and also more prevalent. This is the love of the self. We should not forget that all object-love—that invested in husband or wife, friends, neighbors, brothers and sisters, and even parents—is only the overflow of self-love. We all love ourselves first and last and most. In the normal person, however, experience enables one to see the advantage of drawing upon the treasury of self-love and investing some of it in the love of others; in a vast number of individuals, however, this process is inhibited. For various reasons—sometimes a lack of self-confidence, sometimes a fear of deprecation by others, sometimes because of painful experiences, sometimes because of faulty training—this cannot be done. For such people a true and deep relationship with another person is impossible except on such a basis as feeds this self-love instead of detracting from it. Such persons may fall in love but they fall in love with people who are like themselves, with people who flatter them, who feed their vanity and build up their self-confidence by a constant process of emotional nourishment. If one

[3]Leporello, valet to Don Juan, in Mozart's opera of that name, enumerates in his famous aria the many women who were seduced by his master.

is so much in love with himself, then one cannot accept the role in which he must give love; he can only accept the role in which he is always the recipient of love, like a little child whose self-love is fanned and fed by the attentions of his mother.

In the sexual act, such persons may be at times very potent, particularly if the circumstances of the act are such that their vanity is flattered, their feeling of omnipotence encouraged. This is not real sexual potency, however, and such individuals sooner or later are apt to meet with disaster. They are very proud of their sexual organs and, indeed, it is not inaccurate to say that such persons prefer masturbation to sexual intercourse. Such intercourse as they perform is frequently only a kind of intravaginal masturbation and as such is really a kind of impotency which sooner or later becomes manifest.

The prudishness in regard to sexual matters has placed the treatment of impotence and frigidity under a cloud. On the one hand there are countless sufferers from this affliction who do not know that there is *any* efficacious treatment, while others become the easy prey of quacks and charlatans. Still others are treated by well-meaning but, in my opinion, mistaken physicians who ascribe all impotence and frigidity to physical or chemical factors and use corresponding methods of treatment. It is, as Crookshank[4] has put it in another connection, as if a doctor seeing a woman weeping should label it "paroxysmal lacrimation" and recommend treating it with belladonna and astringents, local applications, restrictions of fluids, a salt-free diet and the avoidance of sexual excess, tea, tobacco and alcohol with the further reservation that

[4] Crookshank, F. G.: Organ Jargon. *British Journal of Medical Psychology*, 10:295-311, January, 1931.

in the event of failure of these measures the surgical removal of the tear glands might be imperative.

Nevertheless it is true that sometimes the suggestive or punitive value of these treatments helps to produce a good result but more often I believe they are utterly futile. A rational method of therapeutic approach would enable the patient to become aware of and repudiate the unconscious influences which act as a deterrent. Those who minimize the seriousness and frustration of impotence and frigidity are unlikely to welcome so considerable and major a treatment program as psychoanalysis entails. They may be too proud to admit their disappointment or they may be reluctant to face the fact that an entire characterological revision is necessary, the impotence or frigidity being but a symptom which they would like to isolate and treat as if it were a trivial inconvenience instead of a significant index.[5]

[5]Many articles in the psychoanalytic literature deal with this subject. Recent and authoritative is Bergler, Edmund: *Die Psychische Impotenz des Mannes,* Berne, Hans Huber, 1937; also, by the same author and E. Hitschman: *Frigidity in Women,* Washington, D.C., Nervous and Mental Disease Publishing Company, 1936.

5.

"What Is Wrong with My Marriage": The Verdict of 100 Women

by G. V. Hamilton, M. D.
and Kenneth Macgowan

This account of marital dissatisfactions is based on Dr. Hamilton's pioneering four-year *Research in Marriage*, which involved intimate examinations of 100 married men and an equal number of married women, including fifty couples. A considerable number of them were persons of outstanding intellectual and artistic achievement; most of them were college graduates between thirty and forty years of age. From their self-revealing answers to a series of 400 questions, the Hamilton report was able to present significant data on the sexual events of childhood and puberty, and relate them to the adult attitudes and patterns of performance of the 200 spouses. Reprinted from *What is Wrong with My Marriage* by G. V. Hamilton, M.D., and Kenneth Macgowan, copyright, 1929, by Albert & Charles Boni, Inc., by permission of the publisher.

See also Chapter 5 in *Women:* " 'What Is Wrong with My Marriage': The Verdict of 100 Men."

I

THE FIRST QUESTION—that bold, bald challenge: "What is there in your marriage that is especially unsatisfactory to you?"—marked the women off sharply from the men. Where thirty-nine husbands had no complaint at all, only twenty-five women came through with a reply of "Nothing." Almost half of the forty-five wives who were happily married found something seriously wrong, where only a quarter of the happy husbands had complained. The men and women produced about the same number of dissatisfactions—well over two hundred—and they had just the same number of different things to complain about—forty-three. But more women than men complained of only one irritation, and more women than men complained of a very large number. One wife had no less than fifteen troubles on her mind, and three others had as many dissatisfactions as the most querulous husband had produced.

The first question brought a sharp and significant explosion. It was undoubtedly the best test of the man's or woman's state of mind. Furthermore, the first complaint that each mentioned seemed to be by far the most important, real, and permanent. In many ways the best picture of what these seventy-five dissatisfied women found wrong with their marriages comes from these first grudges.

Many of the women replied simply and clearly—especially the twenty-five that found nothing unsatisfactory in their marriages. But in a few cases the answer reminded the examiner of the restless bafflement of a person half-awake and physically uncomfortable, who knows that all is not well with him and yet can't quite define or locate his discomfort. These women fumbled and told nothing specific, except that they were oppressed by a sense that the matrimonial situation wasn't right. Here is the sort of fumbling answers that fourteen women gave —somewhat paraphrased and disguised, of course, yet typical:

"I never thought along those lines. Have I got to find something?" . . . "Oh! My! [Then a pause.] I wonder how I can answer that. [Another pause.] I'd almost say that it might be a lack of mental understanding between him and me, so far as I can answer at all. That must be an awfully vague answer." . . . "That's an awfully hard question. I'm afraid I don't know what to do with it."

II

When it came to positive and definite dissatisfactions, troubles over the sexual side of marriage led all the rest by a wide margin. Eighteen women had this uppermost in their minds when they met the first question. Some of their answers were as simple and direct as: "The sexual—that's the fundamental thing." Others had much more to tell, and the way to the truth led through the revelation of many tangled relationships. One woman knew the simple fact that she was sexually cold. Yet in spite of her frigidity, she had an ardent temperament, and she loved her husband. He loved her, and the consequence was all manner of friction. He made demands on her that she wanted to meet and yet could not. She was miserable over her failure, even more miserable than he was hurt and angry. Here is another woman who felt the lack of physical vitality in herself: "It seems to me that I have always been disappointed because I have never felt any passionate attachment to my husband. I felt this lack from the beginning. Affection seems to kill passion for me. He is just the other way, and that makes an impasse." Another woman began: "What a big question!" There was a laugh and a long pause, then: "Our sexual life together was most unsatisfactory. Things did not work out at all, and many little troubles came along as a consequence. In the end I began to feel that my husband was not the sort of man I wanted to live with anyway. He is too fatherly and too concerned with my health. He doesn't seem to me a stimulating person. I don't know why I feel I need stimulation from an outside source."

If the answers of these two hundred men and women mean anything as a reflection of the state of the better educated classes in America, here is food for thought. Out of eighteen wives who complained of lack of satisfaction with the sexual side of marriage, the trouble with no fewer than fourteen of them, as their intimate confidences revealed, lay in their own inadequacy. In the other four cases it was the man's fault. The natures of these fourteen women had been so warped in early childhood by the false puritanism of their parents that they were now incapable of living a full and normal married life. How far does all America's womanhood suffer from the pious sins of the fathers—and mothers?

III

Compared with physical complaints, the temperamental troubles of these women ran a very poor second. Only nine women believed that lack of congeniality in their husbands was the primary trouble. And this was almost a complete reversal of the men's reports. For only twelve husbands put the weight of their married miseries principally on the physical, while sixteen registered temperamental dissatisfactions. There cannot be the slightest question that this all comes back to the simple fact that men are far better constituted than women of the present day to get complete sexual satisfaction out of marriage. Again it should be emphasized that nervous or puritanical parents have been at special pains to blunt and distort, *particularly in their daughters,* those instincts which are necessary to the development of a normal nervous system and a normal physique.

Each of the nine women who complained primarily of uncongenial temperaments said, in one way or another, "There isn't the unity of purpose, outlook, or desire that

I need for my contentment." Some blamed their husbands for this. Some, like this one, did not: "I think the main thing is we don't look at things in the same light. We seldom agree. Mainly it is my fault." Here is a woman who put it completely up to the man: "I have reached a stage where my husband bores me and has bored me for a long time. He is very unstimulating." Another: "The trouble is lack of love for remaining at home, and just being quiet and doing things together. He doesn't make a comrade of me. This troubles me because I think I see a fundamental cause of this in him— something he can't escape from. He is a Spaniard and has this utterly different way of regarding a woman." Sometimes a woman saw faults on both sides, or at least divergent natures that could not be bent together: "There have been different things at different times. Right now, if there is any real difficulty, it is in our make-ups. He is careful and efficient. I am spontaneous and original. Sometimes this causes lack of sympathy and difficult situations. It is usually something he has said that proves his lack of understanding of me. He hasn't the creative kind of mind, the kind that I like. I study causes; he studies effects." There is certainly a little criticism in that comment, but here in the next we have frank displeasure over a husband's shortcomings: "I haven't found him intellectually companionable. He has an entirely different lot of interests. He dislikes one of the children without any real reason, and I think he likes the others better than he does me. He never likes the people I do, and he isn't ready to give my friends any consideration at all. In fact he is rude to them."

A certain number of these complaints on lack of congeniality came back in the end to a re-emphasis on sexual

maladjustments. And to reinforce the importance of the
physical to women—or to the women of this research—
we had seven wives who complained that their husbands
were either unfaithful to them or on the way to be so.
Some of them merely suspected and were tortured; others
knew: "He doesn't care for me any more. He doesn't
want me. I think it's because of this other woman. He
worships our child. He's transferred all his affection to
it, and he has found a wife outside his home." Some of
the women at one time believed in sexual freedom both
for their husbands and themselves. Almost invariably
they could not tolerate their husbands' affairs; though
the husbands—registering no complaints whatever about
their wives' interest in other men—seemed to manage
free love more easily. "I am emotionally unhappy," said
one wife, "at my husband's playing up to other women.
The thing that has annoyed me most is his taking a
lover, even though I took one, too."

It is not at all a bad guess that 5 per cent of the better
educated women of America—like these of this research—
find it very hard to adjust themselves to the duties and
limitations of domesticity. Five women centered their
complaints chiefly on "Kinder" and "Kueche," if not
"Kirche." Just as a similar group of men objected to the
"unfreedom" of matrimony. "I like the domestic part,"
said one woman, "but I hate it, too. I miss my own
work, and yet I like to cook and sew things for the
house. But being tied to it—I hate that." Another: "The
most unsatisfactory part is the monotony of the days.
What you have to look forward to is so—I don't know
what! But you see people who have been married ten or
twenty years, and they are just going to bridges and
teas. That's all there seems to be ahead." "The most unsatisfactory thing," said another woman, "is routine. I

hate it so. The marriage relation itself is all right. It is the conventionality and responsibility that go with it."

IV

Out of these hundred men and women the same num-ber—five—seemed to have acquired mates who were child-ish or undeveloped in their minds and emotions. "Though we have been married a dozen years," said one woman, "my husband hasn't matured. He doesn't seem to me any older than when we got married. That means that I have had to shoulder all the responsibility. He isn't practical. A man who is egoistic without being really self-confident is pretty hard to live with." Another woman had a husband subject to severe depressions: "The trouble lies in my husband's spells of glumness. Last winter he went through a period when he thought he had to have long hours of sleep. This caused an irri-tating discussion. It developed into a depression. He retired into himself as if he had been injured, and then he slept all day. I kept wondering what I had done to hurt him, but I couldn't see."

Children make a source of difficulty for many women—not being able to have them, or the husband's not want-ing them. Four of the women began with this complaint, something that primarily disturbed only two of the men. "I haven't any children. I had a little boy, but I lost him. He doesn't want children. At least, I think so." . . . "I can't have children." . . . "He won't let me have children."

There was one woman who was distressed to find that her husband had turned out to be her child. He wasn't moronic or diseased, but he wasn't a mate. He clung. "My husband never married me. I married him. He is so

much younger than I am, and he is hopelessly imma-
ture."

Three women complained of their husbands' inability
to earn enough money. "The only unsatisfactory thing,"
said one of them, "is that I haven't enough money to
live in comfort. I was really ideally happy in our tiny
apartment until the baby came. Now the three rooms are
so crowded. I'm not holding that against my husband.
He's doing the best he can."

Three other husbands were most decidedly not doing
their best. They were alcoholics, and this was the complaint that first came to the minds of their wives.

One woman was unhappy because her husband was
egregiously selfish. In spite of their love and their common interests, she couldn't be happy, because there was
always this ugly thing staring her in the face.

Another husband was unsatisfactory because he was so
taciturn—"just a clam."

One woman found her husband's family the only fly
in the ointment, but such a large, ever-present, noisome
fly.

One woman who loved her husband almost obsessively
knew that he did not love her. There was no getting
round that fact.

One woman knew that her own ill health interfered
with the success of her married life. She wasn't up to
doing many things with her husband which seemed essential to the happiness of them both. She knew that a
tired wife isn't easy to live with, and that the husband
of such a wife gets to be a little difficult also.

And then there were two women who were like rats
in a trap: "The whole damned thing is so bad I can't
pick one thing and say, 'It's that.'"

V

Of course, some women are downright unlucky in their choice of a husband. It is not a question of a particular man's qualities not suiting a particular woman's tastes. Many women inadvertently select husbands with whom no woman could be happy. Almost 15 per cent of the wives in the research had made this sort of mistake, and could legitimately blame the whole failure of their marriages on their husbands. Is the ratio as high in the whole class of society from which these people came? The three who married alcoholics, the four whose husbands were physically inadequate, the five whose mates were moronic or psychopathic, the one who was tied to an egregiously selfish ass, and the one whose husband remained infantile in his emotional attitudes—all these can be rated as women whose marriages were failures because they had had the bad luck to marry matrimonial incompetents. It doesn't always take two to make a marriage unsuccessful. In these fourteen cases the women might have been paragons of unselfishness, wisdom, and beauty, and yet the fundamental shortcomings of the men would have insured fourteen matrimonial failures.

On the other hand, in the majority of cases, partial or complete failure is probably a joint error, and could be corrected. Out of the seventeen women who found the sexual relation to be wrong in their marriages, fourteen were themselves inadequate. They had never—even during the first glowing days of mating—been able to find complete satisfaction. Perhaps no man could have helped them to an ultimately satisfactory adjustment, yet we know that among the hundred women were several who, at the end of months, even years of mutual effort, at last came into their own.

VI

Another way of analyzing the complaints of these hundred women is to look at those that have *only one* subject of dissatisfaction. There were only fifteen men in this group, but no less than thirty-six women concentrated on a single topic—just as at the other extreme they had outnumbered the men in the variety of troubles which a single wife could enumerate. Here, among the women with only one grievance, the sexual again led all the other sources of dissatisfaction.

Although more than a third of the hundred women were content with just one complaint, the rest more than made up in number and variety of troubles. Perhaps the simplest way of picturing how most of the two hundred and thirty-three complaints were divided, is to combine many of the related troubles under one head and put these down in a table that also compares the answers of the men. Here we have, not one primary complaint from each woman, but a list of all the things the women found wrong:

	Women's Complaints	Men's Complaints
Temperamental dissatisfactions..	37	49
Sexual dissatisfactions..........	30	39
Domestic slavery or lack of personal freedom..............	18	10
Economic troubles.............	16	8
Lack of affection..............	13	0
Jealousy	11	8
Everything wrong..............	10	2
Troubles over children.........	7	8
Ill-health	5	10

Vocational interferences with marriage	5	2
Friction over relatives	4	7
Social life spoiled by marriage ...	2	5
Mate's alcoholism	3	0
Evasive answers	2	0

Here we find temperamental difficulties outnumbering sexual difficulties for the women, but not to the extent they do for the men. Troubles with families, with children, with health, and with the social life also bring out more complaints from the men. But on all the other topics the women have more complaints than the men. It is particularly interesting that five times as many women think the whole marriage hopelessly wrong. But the most astonishing fact in this table certainly is that a dozen women are much exercised over the lack of affection in their marriages, while *not one man expresses any views at all on that subject.*

VII

Most of these women were, like the men, upset over more than one thing. Let us try to separate them out a bit on the basis of how many complained of one thing but were totally oblivious of another. Most comparisons of this sort work out very much as in the cases of the men, except that the women place more emphasis on the physical than on the temperamental. There aren't half as many women as men upset over *both* the physical and the temperamental. They seem to keep those two things straighter in their minds. They don't confuse so much what they want.

But on the subject of jealousy the women show a very striking difference. Now every man who brought up

jealousy, also complained of temperamental troubles,
and three-quarters of the jealous men were dissatisfied
sexually. Only half of the jealous women complained
about temperament, and not one of them was sexually
dissatisfied. It is not too wild a guess that men are more
apt to grow jealous when they find a wife unresponsive
because unsatisfied in her sex life, and women are more
apt to pay attention to possible rivals when the thing at
stake is satisfactory and highly prized. The fact that the
men were not so prone to jealousy as the women came
out sharply where couples had granted each other freedom to indulge in outside "affairs." The men tolerated
their wives' adulteries very well. The women might accept the same situation intellectually but they could not
go through with it emotionally.

VIII

The men and the women of this study disagreed sharply about the intellectual and social qualifications of their
mates and the success of their marriages along those
lines. In answering the first question the men were far
more critical about this than their wives. Only two
women blamed their husbands or their marriages for
dooming them to an unsatisfactory social life, against
five men who complained. Only three women found
their husbands lacking in those capacities which make
for intellectual, social or vocational advancement, where
eleven men accused their wives of such failings.

A special question—"Are you and your wife socially
and intellectually well-mated, or otherwise?"—developed
the fact that the women weren't so sure as the men that
they were socially well-mated. Twice as many women
saw themselves socially ill-mated. They were also more
critical about the intellectual success of their marriages,

but the difference wasn't so sharp. The interesting point here is that the women were keener on the social question and more aware of social and intellectual disparities, but that this didn't weigh so much in the scales of dissatisfaction. Again, we have a "spiritual" value that was not so important as the physical and the material.

IX

The women knew much better than the men just when they first began to be dissatisfied with something in their mates. Only eight were uncertain, against thirteen men. Remember also that more women were dissatisfied than men. Consequently there were fifty-three women who could place the date of dissatisfaction, against only forty-three men. Yet in spite of this, the men who found dissatisfaction before the end of the first year of married life exceeded the women thirty-one to twenty-six. In the next five years, however, three times as many women as men began to be unhappy, and it was not until after the sixth year that the men began to catch up. The men, driven to marriage by a much more direct and simple physical urge, confessed to doubts about their mates even during the engagement period—seven critically-minded males to only one woman—but they went right on. They grew still more critical in the first few months of marriage. The women seemed to marry in a state of vague desire for love, uncritical and unsure. They spent five years learning to feel and to know. It was only then—a little late, no doubt—that they were able to separate passion and judgment. Something of the sort can be safely said of most women.

X

The first question on the dissatisfactions of marriage

came back at later periods of the research. So far as the
women were concerned, familiarity did not breed any
more contempt than they already felt. The men had
grown steadily more critical after the first plunge. The
second question of this sort—perhaps because it asked
what was the principal cause of *"trouble"* between husband and wife, instead of speaking placidly of mere
"dissatisfactions"—brought the women up sharp against
the idea of serious, possibly disastrous friction. Where
this treatment increased the number of complaining men
from sixty-one to sixty-three, it reduced the critical wives
from seventy-five to sixty-three. When the question took
the form of asking what most annoyed and dissatisfied,
the women jumped back to seventy-nine and the men
went with them as far as seventy-seven.

After a series of questions on marital economics and
the effect of relatives on the married life, came three
questions which give us some sense of how far the men
and women were consciously content to go on living in
a state of matrimony—even their own state. First they
were asked if they wished to go on living with their
mates because they loved them. Exactly the same number
of women who had found serious dissatisfactions with
their husbands now declared they would go on living
with them for love. Three more men than women were
willing to continue for this reason. Ten women and
eleven men would not part because separation or divorce
was against their principles, and ten men and ten women
—many of them the same as those with principles against
divorce—wanted to stick because a break-up might in-
jure their business or social standing. Only fifty-six wom-
en, against seventy men, wanted to stay together because
the other spouse would be unhappy without her. Still
fewer women would tolerate matrimony for the sake of

the children—fifty-three women to sixty-two men. The women who did not wish to go on living with their mates on account of love, children, or a feeling of loyalty far outnumbered the men.

Next came the odd, arresting and very engaging query: "If by some miracle you could press a button and find that you had never been married to your husband would you press that button?" When this was sprung on the men a particularly unhappy husband who had just turned on the desk light, shot his hand back to the electric button and turned the light off again. Only sixteen of his fellows followed him by word of mouth. Sixteen women were likewise ready for a new deal. The next question asked whether, knowing what they now know, these men and women would wish to marry if they were unmarried. Eight women said, "No," and nine men.

Finally, toward the end of the examination, came a question which asked once more for the sources of dissatisfaction. But it asked frankly and firmly just what matters of this sort had made the marriage a failure. At the word "failure," the solid majority of the dissatisfied men melted away. There were only twenty-eight members of the opposition who were willing to admit that the marriage had been unsuccessful. The women's party held out. Its numbers shrank very noticeably, but at the end there were forty-two wives more or less calmly voting their marriages unsuccessful, and ready to give a bill of particulars. Close to the end of this long self-examination only fifty-eight women believed themselves happily married to any degree, while seventy-two men still voted their marriages successful.

Here are the answers to the six crucial questions placed in tabular form:

61 men and 75 women found something "especially un-
    satisfactory"

63 men and 65 women found a "source of trouble"

77 men and 79 women found something to "annoy or
    dissatisfy"

22 men and 25 women said they did not love their mates
    enough to want to go on living with them

34 men and 36 women said they would end their mar-
    riages if they could do so by pressing a button

37 men and 53 women said their marriages were failures

The sudden and firm pessimism of the women over the
failure of their marriages was truly startling. Was this
feminine cynicism? Was it the emotionalism of woman
headed, for the moment, toward gloom? Or were the men
exhibiting a broad streak of optimism and chivalry?

The examiner was pretty well convinced that the men
were acting along lines laid down for them in earliest
youth. An echo of "She's your mother, my boy!" still
rang in their ears as they thought of the women who
had replaced for them the image of their goddess of
childhood. Loyalty and chivalry, consideration for the
weaker and the more dependent—these things turned
them sentimentally optimistic at the word "failure."

As for the women—it was good, solid, realistic observation.

Proof? By means of all the millions of words and
thousands of intimate personal details brought out by
the four hundred questions, the examiner was able at
the end to form a pretty accurate estimate of the degree
of satisfaction which these men and women had actually
found in their married lives—quite apart from what they
preferred to think for themselves. Fifty-one men and
forty-five women made the grade; their marriages were

successful. Yet, if it had been left to the optimism of the men, seventy-two husbands would have denied that their marriages were unsuccessful—twenty-one of them with no justification. On the other hand fifty-eight women looked on the bright side of the marriage question—only thirteen more than should have done so. Women live more by their emotions, and sometimes live straighter.

You may think that this is due to the fact that the whole group of men and women did not match up as they might have if they had all been married to one another. Let us look at the records of the fifty-five men and women who did enter the research as couples.

Twenty-five couples had equal grades of satisfaction. In ten couples the husbands were more dissatisfied than the wives. But in the twenty others the wives were more dissatisfied than the husbands. These same men and women had voted on the success of their own marriages much along the lines of the rest of the two hundred.

XI

If we summed up at this point the matrimonial state of the hundred wives, we should have perhaps three main conclusions. And we might be daring enough to add that they are about as true of the large body of intelligent civilized women as of the hundred special guinea pigs of this research.

If we get right down to the one outstanding difficulty of married life for these women, it is the sexual relationship. If we want to add another that seems almost always present as a subject of complaint—though perhaps it is only a handy peg for hanging a grudge based on some deeper dissatisfaction—it is economic worry. Physical and material troubles, both of them.

If we try to describe the outstanding psychological

quality of these women, it is a great sensitiveness—a far greater sensitiveness than in men. More of them say everything is wrong. They see greater dissatisfactions. They see far more difficulties. They particularize very elaborately. They run to extremes in judgment; more women than men confine themselves to a single source of complaint, and yet more women than men turn in a dozen or more criticisms of their husbands. Though the women are more disturbed about sex than are the men, their peculiarly complex and delicate consciousnesses seek a substitute for the purely physical in this matter of affection which the women alone complained about. And yet, for all this array of sensitiveness—which ought to express itself, the average person would say, in an absorption in spiritual values—these women are intent on physical and material troubles far more than the men. And they are extremely realistic in their ability to recognize and admit matrimonial failure where men assume the pose of a sentimental ostrich.

6.
Physiology of Reproduction

by F. H. A. Marshall

An inquiry into the sexual experience of men and women would be incomplete without some consideration of their essential biological resources. The influence of the genital organs and their internal secretions on general bodily health, their function in the basic act of sex and the ensuing process of birth, are covered here by a distinguished British biologist. Dr. Marshall, Fellow of Christ's College, Cambridge, is the author of a standard work on physiology. Reprinted from *Sex in Social Life*, edited by Sybil Neville-Rolfe, copyright, 1950, by W. W. Norton & Company, Inc., by permission of the publisher.

See also Chapters 6, 7, 12 in *Women*: "Natural Childbirth," "Some Problems of Motherhood," "Menopause: The 'Change of Life.'"

I. The Organs of Reproduction

Physiology is the branch of science which is concerned with the functions performed by living things. It is a department of biology, which embraces the whole science of life. But since physiology deals with function rather than form it is the science which teaches us more particularly the way in which both the body as a whole and its separate parts work, and the laws which govern its various activities. In so doing it may help us to regulate these activities, and by teaching us about the normal working of the body it may show us how any of its parts may be adjusted when they get out of order.

Physiology must always be studied in close relation to anatomy, the department of biology which deals with the form and structure of organisms and their parts, since it is impossible to acquire an insight into functional activity without first possessing some knowledge of the composition and structural relations of the parts of which the organism is composed. Consequently, before attempting to describe the physiology of the organs of reproduction and the successive phases which they undergo in order to fulfill their functions, it is desirable to possess some knowledge of the anatomy of these organs. In supplying this, however, it will be convenient to mention the more obvious functions which the organs are known to discharge.

It will be realized that the genital organs cannot discharge their proper functions without the due co-operation of the other essential organs of the body. In common with all the other parts of the body they depend upon the alimentary system which supplies the body with nourishment, the respiratory system which enables it to breathe, the excretory system which gets rid of waste matter, the circulatory system which carries the blood throughout the body, and the muscular and nervous systems which co-ordinate the activities of the living organism. Without them the genital organs could not receive the necessary nutriment, oxygen, or other essential substances, or be maintained in conditions in which they habitually operate.

The reproductive system, though essential for the continuity of the life of the species, is—unlike the other systems—not essential for the maintenance of the life of the individual. This must not be taken to imply that the reproductive organs do not influence bodily health; as we shall see, certain substances (the internal secretions) which the sex glands discharge into the blood are necessary for the full development of body and mind, and to some extent for the maintenance of vigor. It is, however,

possible to remove all the reproductive organs without
destroying life, and, provided those supplying internal
secretions are retained, to prevent them from discharging
their reproductive functions without seriously affecting
health.

Male Reproductive Organs

The human male reproductive organs consist external-
ly of the testes (or testicles) and the penis. The testes lie
in the scrotum, which is a skin pouch suspended between
the penis and the anus, or rectal opening. It contains
two cavities, separated from each other by a membrane.
Each cavity carries one testis, or testicle, and is connected
with the main cavity of the abdomen through a canal,
called the inguinal canal.

This canal is not empty, nor are the testes isolated
organs. They are connected with the rest of the body
through the spermatic cord, which passes through the
inguinal canal. The spermatic cord is a band of tissue in
which are embedded the blood vessels and nerves that
supply the testes. A tube or duct, called the *vas deferens,*
which originates at the testes, also passes through each
inguinal canal. The vas deferens has the most important
function of providing a passage for the semen, the fluid
containing the spermatozoa, as the male reproductive
elements are called. More will be said of it later.

The testes descend from the abdominal cavity into the
scrotum in late embryonic life by traversing the inguinal
canal. They may fail to complete this descent from their
original position, remaining in the abdominal cavity, or,
more frequently, may traverse part only of the distance
to the scrotum. Thus the testes may reach the groin
without passing through the inguinal canal; in this
position they may give rise to much discomfort or

pain. This condition of incomplete descent is known as cryptorchism, and nearly always causes sterility. It is capable of remedy by surgical treatment.

The testis proper consists of a large number of fine threadlike canals, or tubules. Each canal is lined by cells which produce the spermatozoa, or sperms. It is one of the two main tasks of the testes to produce vast numbers of spermatozoa, which, as it were, bud off the inside wall of the tubules, and are shed into the fluid secreted by certain of the lining cells. They are produced in enormous numbers, and it has been estimated that a single emission contains normally as many as 240 million spermatozoa.

Prior to ejaculation the spermatozoa have to be removed from the testis, and transported to the epididymis, which is the main storehouse of spermatozoa. Their transport is effected by a system of ducts called the *vasa efferentia*. There are twelve on each side, and they open into the corresponding epididymis, which is a long single coiled duct whose coils are so tightly bound that, like the testis, it appears to be a solid organ. The two epididymides are closely associated with the testes; they stretch along their sides, and can be felt by applying the fingers to the front and back of the scrotum.

The wall of the duct that forms the epididymis contains muscle fibers. When these contract, the lumen, as the inner hollow of the duct is called, narrows and the spermatozoa are impelled forward into the vas deferens, which is continuous with the epididymis. Such contraction probably only takes place, normally, during the sex act. In this way the semen is conveyed from each epididymis, by a vas deferens, through the inguinal canal to the urethra, or common urogenital passage. The walls of the vasa deferentia also possess muscle fibers which enable

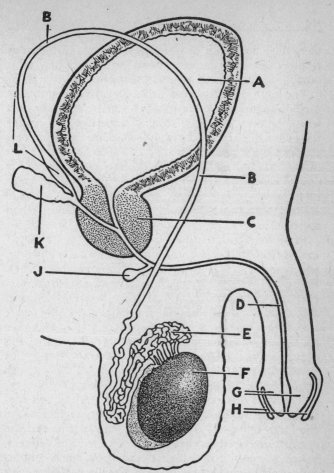

SIDE VIEW (DIAGRAMMATIC) OF THE MALE
GENITAL ORGANS

A = Bladder   E = Epididymis   J = Cowpers Gland
B = Vas Deferens F = Testes   K = Seminal Vesicle
C = Prostate   G = Glans Penis   L = Ampulla
D = Urethra   H = Prepuce or Foreskin

them to contract and thus to send on their contents.

The urethra, or urogenital passage, so-called because it receives both the product of the genital organs and the urine from the bladder, penetrates the penis and thus makes possible the final discharge of the spermatozoa after their long passage. This discharge takes place, as a rule, during the sex act, and is commonly called ejaculation. The fluid containing the spermatozoa is added to in its progress from the testes to the exterior. What leaves the opening of the penis during ejaculation is a composite fluid called semen, or seminal fluid, in which the original fluid with the spermatozoa is the most important but not the most voluminous constituent. Semen consists mainly of various liquid secretions produced by a number of glands and mingling during (or sometimes after) ejaculation.

The glands which contribute to the seminal fluid—in addition to the testes, which actually produce the spermatozoa—are the seminal vesicles and the prostate. The two seminal vesicles are situated one on either side, at the ends of the vasa deferentia near their junction with the urethra. The vesicles open into the urethra. The prostate is a tubular gland surrounding the urethra at the base of the bladder. It discharges its liquid secretion through ducts opening into the urethra. This gland can give rise to serious trouble in middle-aged or old men. Among other changes, it may increase in size and compress the urethra, which passes through it, thereby impeding the flow of urine and necessitating the surgical removal of the gland. The function of the viscid secretion of the prostate gland is not certainly known. It is suggested that it excites movement in the spermatozoa, and also that it cleanses the urethra prior to ejaculation.

Other organs which contribute to the seminal fluid are

the small glands of Cowper and Littré—both named after distinguished anatomists. The former are situated near the exterior of the urethra, into which they open through two fine ducts; the glands of Littré, which are very small, are situated in the lining of the urethra. The wall of the vas deferens itself contributes a small quantity of liquid to the bulk of the semen.

The seminal fluid serves primarily as a carrier of spermatozoa. There is, however, some reason to believe that it is something more than a neutral medium in which spermatozoa can be passed from the body of the male to that of the female. It would seem, for instance, that, as already said, the prostatic secretion stimulates the movement of the spermatozoa (a most important feature of their subsequent behavior) or even that the very fact of the movement taking place depends on the stimulating action of the secretion.

The most complex organ among the highly involved structures of the male reproductive organs is the penis. Its complexity is related to its twofold function of conducting the urine to the exterior through the urethral channel, and conveying the semen into the genital passages of the female. For the most part, it serves simply as the protective wall of the urogenital passage through which the urine is discharged; and while it is fulfilling this function or is entirely at rest is a flaccid, flexible organ. But in order that the urogenital passage may assume its other role, that of transporting semen, the penis hardens and lengthens—undergoes erection, as it is called —so that it may be able to penetrate the female genital passage.

Erection and hardening are brought about by an internal machinery extremely simple as to its nature but extremely complex in its details. Erection is essentially a hydraulic process; just as water, distending a hosepipe, will render the latter resistant to pressure, so blood is used to harden the penis. The wall of the penis contains three cavities, the two *corpora cavernosa,* which are placed one on each side, and are united in the middle line, and the *corpus spongiosum,* which is situated internally and surrounds the urethra. These cavities are normally supplied with blood at all times; and, as is the case with other organs and tissues, the blood flows through them, entering by one and leaving through another set of vessels. Erection takes place when, under the influence of sexual excitement, the local blood supply is increased, and the nerves concerned shut the gate through which the incoming blood can escape. Thus the cavities of the penis retain the full pressure of the blood which enters and the whole penis stiffens.

Female Reproductive Organs

The female organs of reproduction, unlike those of the male, are almost entirely within the body. The chief are the ovaries, the Fallopian tubes, the uterus or womb, and the vagina. The ovaries are a pair of organs lying in the lower part of the cavity of the abdomen which is called the pelvis. A band of tissue called the broad ligament stretches across the pelvis and to it the ovaries, the Fallopian tubes and the uterus are attached. Each ovary, as shown in microscopic sections, is formed of a ground substance or connective tissue, which contains a large number of round structures of varying size known as the Graafian follicles. The smallest of these—the primordial follicles—have no cavity, but consist each of an egg or ovum, surrounded by a row of round cells; these lie just below the surface of the ovary.

The ova in nearly all mammals are microscopic in size.

Throughout reproductive life there is a constant activity going on in the ovary, especially in the follicles. The follicles increase in size and pass inwards to the center of the ovary, the follicular cells multiply and a space is formed between those immediately surrounding the ova and the outer cells which line the wall of the follicle just inside the connective tissue. This space becomes filled with a nutrient fluid called the *liquor folliculi*. Each follicle usually contains one ovum (rarely two or more). The largest follicles occupy a considerable part of a section through the ovary, and as they reach maturity come to protrude visibly from the surface.

In animals which produce large litters the ovaries may assume the appearance somewhat of a bunch of small grapes, each grape representing a follicle. In women, however, only one follicle and ovum usually ripen at a time (occasionally two ova, rarely three or more). It has been calculated that during her reproductive life, which on average extends approximately between the ages of fifteen and forty-five, not more than 400 mature eggs are produced by a woman, an incomparably smaller number than that of the spermatozoa produced by a man. When the ovum is ripe the follicle ruptures and the ovum escapes into the cavity of the pelvis. The ovaries during reproductive life contain yellow pigmented bodies known as the *corpora lutea,* which are produced by an active growth in the follicle after the ovum has escaped.

The Fallopian tubes, or oviducts, the function of which is to convey the ova to the interior of the uterus, open internally into the pelvic cavity close to each ovary. The discharged ova enter the open ends of the tubes, which are expanded in a trumpet-like manner and which are believed to become still more open and to become erect so as to receive the ova as they are released. The

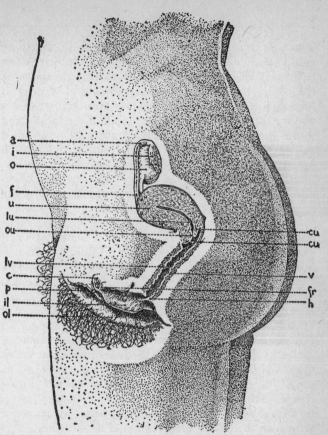

Side view of the female reproductive organs. The parts are shown in partial section and are isolated from neighboring structures in order to indicate their extent in comparison with the body as a whole, the last being represented as transparent near the organs. *a*, ampulla of Fallopian tube; *c*, clitoris; *cu*, cervix of uterus; *f*, Fallopian tube; *fr*, frenulum of the clitoris; *h*, hymen; *i*, infundibulum; *il*, inner lip (labium minor); *lu*, lumen of uterus; *lv*, lumen of vagina; *o*, ovary; *ol*, outer lip (labium major); *ou*, external os of uterus; *p*, prepuce; *u*, uterus (fundus); *v*, vagina.

tubes in the human female are about four inches long.

The uterus lies behind the urinary bladder. It is the organ in which the child develops during pregnancy. In the human female it is a single hollow organ and the Fallopian tubes open into its upper corners. The virgin uterus in the human female is about three inches long, but it subsequently enlarges greatly, especially during pregnancy. The lower part is called the cervix, or neck. It is separated from the corpus or body by a constriction, the communication being called the internal os or mouth. The lower end of the cervix projects somewhat into the vagina, in which it opens by the external os or mouth. A section across the uterus shows a central cavity lined by a smooth membrane, the mucous membrane. This contains a number of glands. Outside the mucous membrane are the muscle layers, and on the outside of all is the smooth external lining of the organ.

The vagina, into which the penis penetrates during copulation, extends from the uterus to the exterior opening. Its walls contain muscle fibers, and internally it is lined by a mucous membrane. It opens to the exterior between the *nymphae,* the two lips which on each side close the aperture, and which lie inside the larger lips called the *labia majora.*

The female sex organs which are visible from the exterior are known collectively as the vulva, both the labia majora and the nymphae being included under this term. The labia majora on the outside are covered with hair. On separating the internal lips or nymphae the vaginal opening becomes visible, and, in front of this, the opening of the urethra through which the urine is ejaculated. The vaginal opening is surrounded by a membrane called the hymen. In the virgin the vaginal opening is usually small. At copulation the hymen is ruptured, and this results in a permanent increase in the size of the vaginal opening. At the upper (anterior) end of the vulva is the clitoris, which is a solid rodlike organ corresponding to the penis of the male, but not perforated by a channel. The clitoris is a sensitive erectile organ, covered by a prepuce or foreskin like the penis, but considerably smaller than that organ. From it erectile tissue extends around the vaginal opening and beneath the skin of the nymphae. These tissues become much congested during sexual intercourse and the process of congestion forms part of what is called the female orgasm. The perineum lies between the vulva and the anus in the same position as in the male.

The Reproductive Elements

The gonads, that is, the testes in the male and the ovaries in the female, are the essential organs of reproduction, since they give rise to the reproductive elements, the spermatozoa and the ova. These organs, as has been mentioned, also produce chemical substances which are secreted into the circulating blood, and are responsible for the distinctive characters of each sex as well as for the series of changes that occur in the reproductive and correlated organs and structures in the successive phases of the sexual cycle. The accessory organs of reproduction, of which in the female the uterus is the most important, are also dependent for their growth, development, and cyclical activity upon the internal secretions of the gonads.

In sexual intercourse the spermatozoa first enter the vagina and thence pass, partly by their own power of activity and partly perhaps through the agency of the muscles of the uterus and the cilia lining the cavity of that organ, upwards throughout the entire length of the uterus, and into the oviducts or Fallopian tubes. Here they normally meet with the eggs which have recently been discharged from one or both of the ovaries, and fertilization is effected by the union of a male with a female cell (spermatozoon with ovum).

The fertilized egg then passes down the tube into the cavity of the uterus, in the meantime commencing to undergo the process of cellular division which marks the development of the new individual. After a short interval the developing ovum enters into an intimate relation with the mother by becoming connected with the wall of the uterus. It develops round it a nourishing membrane— the chorion—which puts out an immense number of minute rootlets by which it is attached during the period of pregnancy. These chorionic rootlets enter into a very close relation with the maternal tissue and the blood vessels of the uterus, from which they draw the nutriment for the growing ovum. The organ which is formed by the chorion and its rootlets on the one hand, and the maternal tissues on the other, is called the placenta. Throughout pregnancy it is for the developing child an organ of nutrition, excretion and respiration. The child during its intrauterine development is enclosed within a bag filled with fluid and is connected with the placenta by the umbilical cord, which is severed immediately after birth.

II. Periodic Changes

Menstruation

In most animals the organs of reproduction undergo regular alternations of rest and activity correlated with nonbreeding and breeding seasons. That is to say, there is generally an internal rhythm of reproduction.

In the human male the spermatozoa are produced in the testes continuously throughout the whole year, and fertile coition can take place at any time, though there may be variation in sexual potency or in the number of spermatozoa which are formed and ejaculated. In the female, however, there is typically a menstrual cycle of about one lunar month. This cycle depends upon an inherent rhythm and recurs in correlation with sexual changes in all the organs of reproduction.

The uterine changes which mark the menstrual cycle consist of four chief stages: (1) A constructive stage in which the organs undergo growth (about twelve days); (2) a destructive stage of very variable intensity, in which some of the blood vessels give way and bleeding takes place through the vagina to the exterior, accompanied by some destruction of tissue which also comes away forming with the blood the "menstrual clot" (four days); (3) a stage of repair or regeneration during which the bleeding organ heals up and becomes restored (seven days); and (4) a stage of quiescence (five days).

The constructive stage during which the uterus undergoes considerable growth resembles in many respects the changes which occur at the beginning of pregnancy, and the destructive stage which supervenes may be regarded as the removal of the tissue which is so prepared if no fertilized ovum is present.

Just as there is a variation in the length of the menstrual cycle, so also there may be a considerable difference in the severity of the menstrual process within the limits of the normal. It may be characteristic of particular individuals to discharge a considerable quantity of blood and tissue in the composition of the menstrual clot, whereas other individuals may only experience a slight discharge. The complete absence of menstruation, in any but a pregnant woman or one who is nursing her child, must be regarded as abnormal. During the nursing period, menstruation occurs in about 40 per cent of cases; it is nearly always resumed shortly after the cessation of nursing, or within two months of the birth of the child, if the infant is not breast fed. Menstruation, or a bleeding which resembles it, may continue during pregnancy without interfering with the development of the embryo; but if this state is found medical advice should be sought.

While the above processes are going on in the uterus a series of changes is likewise taking place in the ovaries. The ovarian follicles, as we have seen, undergo a gradual development throughout the whole of reproductive life. This development is so timed that each month one, or rarely more than one, becomes ripe. Where more than one ovum is shed twins, triplets, or quadruplets may occur.

The rupture of the follicle and discharge of the ovum is called ovulation. This process is believed to occur typically about the fourteenth day of the cycle, that is, fourteen days after the beginning of the menstrual discharge. According to one view, however, it would be more correct to state that ovulation occurs fourteen days before the end of the cycle, and this irrespective of the length of the cycle, which, as we have seen, although typically twenty-eight days, may be rather less or more.

It would appear, then, that the greatest chance of conception is in the middle of the cycle, or, to be more precise, just before the middle. This view is only correct, however, on the assumption that the ova and spermatozoa are capable of maintaining themselves alive and fertile for a short time only after their release from the gonads. This assumption is justified by all experimental data. For instance, it is known that in the rabbit the spermatozoa lose their capacity for fertilization about thirty hours after release, and the ova after about six hours.

It would seem likely that there are prolonged periods during the cycle when coition will prove sterile. Nevertheless, such so-called "safe periods" cannot be relied on, because of the uncertainty in particular individuals as to when ovulation occurs. In order to obtain knowledge of the periods of fertility in a particular individual it is first necessary to ascertain the normal duration of that individual's cycle.

After ovulation the discharged ovarian follicle becomes converted into a so-called "yellow body," or *corpus luteum*. The conversion is effected very rapidly. The cells which previously lined the wall increase in size and other cells multiply so that an ingrowth of tissues into the former cavity takes place; and this ingrowth continues until nearly the whole of the cavity is filled by a vast number of yellow cells forming the yellow body. If conception occurs, the corpus luteum persists throughout a considerable part of the period of pregnancy, but if the ovum fails to become fertilized the uterus begins to regress after about a fortnight, and at the end of the month is reduced to little more than a scar. During the period of this activity the corpus luteum contains a yellow pigment (lutein), but in a later stage this disappears, and the final form of the corpus luteum may be a structureless body with degenerate cells (the *corpus albicans*).

Pregnancy

The ovum is usually fertilized in the upper part of the oviduct. A single spermatozoon effects the act of fertilization, and the remainder of the spermatozoa die somewhere in the female passages. The enormous development of the uterus during pregnancy has been already alluded to; apart from the developing young (the foetus) and its membranes the previously virgin uterus increases in size during the first pregnancy about thirty times. It is only after the third month of pregnancy that the dimensions of the uterus have been increased to such an extent that the organ rises from the pelvic cavity so as to reach the cavity of the abdomen. By the end of the sixth month the uterus is extended as far as the umbilicus or navel. By the end of pregnancy the uterus has reached the ribs and the pit of the stomach. The alimentary canal and other organs are pushed to one side in the process of enlargement, and this change sometimes produces constipation, while in the later stages of pregnancy pressure on the bladder may cause frequent passing of urine. The general distension often causes a kind of cracking of the skin in the abdominal region.

The nonoccurrence of menstruation is one of the signs of pregnancy. Other well-known indications are the sensations of nausea sometimes followed by vomiting (the "morning sickness") which commonly occur from the second to the third or fourth month but not afterward. The vulva may be congested and slight pigmentation may occur on the forehead and cheeks, as well as round the nipples. There is sometimes an enlargement of the thyroid gland in the neck. (A similar enlargement may occur at menstruation.) Apart from the enlargement of the abdomen the most characteristic visible change in pregnancy is the development of the mammary glands. The breasts begin to swell early in pregnancy, but true milk is not secreted until the second to the fifth day after birth. A diagnostic test of great value is the presence in the urine within a few weeks of the onset of pregnancy of certain chemical substances.

The period of pregnancy does not necessarily involve discomfort; in fact many women have a sense of increased well-being, and their number would be much greater if nutritive and other environmental circumstances were always favorable. Pregnancy does not necessitate change in the general mode of living, and in particular does not demand interruption of normal sexual intercourse except toward the end.

The average duration of pregnancy is estimated at 280 days or ten lunar months. It is reckoned from conception, or, where this is not known, from the cessation of menstruation. Prolongation of pregnancy sometimes occurs, but premature birth is far commoner. Expulsion of the child before the seventh month (miscarriage or abortion) rarely results in a living child, but premature birth after the beginning of the seventh month is frequently successful.

The Development of the Embryo

As soon as the ovum is fertilized by a spermatozoon it begins a series of cell divisions. This is the first stage of the development of all types of ova, and is known as the period of cleavage. While the first cleavages are occurring, the ovum continues its journey toward the uterus. When this is at length reached, the segmented ovum attaches itself to the uterine wall, and as it were burrows into it, actually digesting and absorbing some of the tissues of the mother. This process is absolutely necessary for the survival of the new individual, since the human ovum is provided with very little reserve nourishment in the form of yolk; it can only support its own life for the short period of cleavage, and must then become dependent on the mother for the essential food materials. The menstrual cycle, with its accompanying changes in the internal organs of the female, is so timed that, after each ovulation, the uterus is built up into a condition suitable to receive and nourish the ovum if fertilization occurs.

The earliest stages in the development of the ovum, after it has become attached to the uterine wall, are still not all fully understood. We know, however, that as the cleavage stage of the fertilized egg proceeds further and further, the mass of cells forms a ball of which the surface is rather furry, as the cells penetrate among those of the uterine wall in which the embryo lies, while the interior has a spongy texture. In the middle of the spongy mass two cavities, filled with fluid, appear lying quite near one another with a solid plate of cells between them. It is in this plate that the body of the new individual appears, and for that reason the plate is spoken of as the embryonic area, while all the rest of the cells derived from the fertilized ovum belong to the extra-embryonic region. These latter take no part in the formation of the child's body, but develop into structures which aid the embryo in obtaining its nourishment from the mother.

At first the embryo is a very simple affair, not very like a human being. At the very earliest time when it can be recognized among the surrounding spongy tissues, it consists of three flat layers of cells piled one above the other. The topmost of these is known as ectoderm, and will form the skin and nerves; the middle one is the mesoderm, and will form the muscles and heart, while the third and lowest is the endoderm, which will give rise to the stomach, intestines, lungs, liver, and other internal organs.

These three layers can be recognized as a first stage in the development of nearly all animals. Very soon the young human lays down the ground plan of its body; part of the ectoderm folds in along a line which corresponds to the middle of the back, and thus forms the beginning of the brain and spinal cord, while on each side of this the mesoderm aggregates into a row of lumps which are the forerunners of the vertebrae of the backbone, and the endoderm underneath begins to fold up into a tube which represents the gut.

All these changes are over in about a month, by which time the embryo has its fundamental structures laid down in outline. But the outline is still only very rough and schematic; there are innumerable details to be filled in before the individual is ready to be born. It is still extremely small—only about a quarter of an inch long. The events of its growth, and the gradual addition of more organs and the developing complexity of those which are already present make too long a story to be told here. There is one further incident, however, which may be mentioned, since it is one which many people have heard something of, and which also provides a good example of a very interesting general principle about the process of development.

During the second month the embryonic head and body are fairly well formed, although the limbs are only just beginning to appear, and the whole embryo has a rather wormlike shape. Behind the head, in the neck region, a series of folds appears on each side, and these bend in until they may actually break through from the outside into the throat. This is just the place where gill-slits appear in fish, and a careful study of the folds in human embryos shows that they do in fact correspond to fish gill-slits. This is a somewhat surprising fact, since human embryos never need to use gills as a respiratory apparatus. Actually, these slits eventually become quite different things, such as glands, and a very short examination of the human "gill-slits" is sufficient to show that they could not possibly function as gills; they are not built like the slits of adult fish, but only like those of embryo fish in which the development is just beginning.

The only satisfactory theory of why they should be formed in the human embryo is provided by the theory of evolution. If we suppose that man, like other mammals, is evolved from a fishlike ancestor, it seems reasonable that as evolution proceeded and new types of animal appeared, the development of these new types should not be completely different from that of their ancestors but merely modifications of it. The fish embryo must develop gill-slits, because the adult will need gills; and the descendants of fish start, as it were, with the possibility of developing gill-slits, and will continue to do so provided the embryonic slits are eventually transformed into something which is useful in the new circumstances. The embryos of more highly evolved animals therefore tend to resemble the embryos of their evolutionary ancestors.

We must turn now to the development of the extra-embryonic portions of the fertilized egg. As is well known, the human embryo, like that of all mammals, is kept alive by its contact with the mother. The maternal organism must provide for the foetus within her uterus in several different ways. Food substances and oxygen must be passed to it, but it is almost equally important that the waste products formed in the embryo by the normal processes of life should be removed. This exchange of substances does not utilize any of the normal openings of the embryonic body, which is not fed through its mouth and does not excrete through the urinary and anal openings. The exchange takes place directly between the maternal and embryonic bloods. This does not mean that blood actually passes from the mother into the embryo and back again. What happens is that a special organ is formed in which the mother's blood is brought very close to that of the embryo, so that the two fluids are only separated by a thin film of cells, through which it is fairly easy for food substances and oxygen to diffuse toward the embryo while waste products diffuse away from it.

This organ, as we have previously seen, is called the placenta. It is really made up of two parts. One of these is the maternal part, which is formed from the tissue of the wall of the uterus. The other part is the embryonic component, and this is formed from the extraembryonic tissues evolved in the developing ovum. In its first stages this extraembryonic tissue forms a hollow bag, in which the actual embryo is suspended by a short stalk. As time goes on, the stalk lengthens, and becomes the umbilical cord; blood vessels run through it, and in the region where the stalk joins the surface of the bag, the walls of the bag thicken, to become the embryonic part of the placenta.

In the first two months the embryo acquires a length of about one and one-fifth inches. After this time it is usually called a foetus.

Parturition or the Process of Birth

During the later stages of pregnancy, and more particularly in the final week or two, the uterus shows an increasing irritability, which displays itself in contractions which do not give rise to pain. With the approach of actual labor the contractions become more intense and painful, and the foetal membranes, distended with fluid, are forced into the neck of the uterus (*cervix uteri*), which becomes dilated, a few small vessels being torn, and some blood discharged. Next, the longitudinal muscles of the uterus contract and cause the mouth *(os uteri)* to open.

The contraction of these muscles marks the first stage in parturition, or the act of giving birth. The body of the uterus, the neck and the opening then form a continuous passage. The foetal membranes commonly rupture at this time, but occasionally remain intact until after birth, the child then being born inside its "caul."

In the second stage of labor all the uterine muscles contract forcibly and the child is expelled from the uterus to the vagina and thence to the exterior. This is effected by the contraction of the muscles of the abdomen and the diaphragm, which contract simultaneously with those of the uterus. The vagina is very yielding and the passage of the child is facilitated by the secretion of mucus.

The birth of the child marks the end of the second stage of labor. The uterine contractions then cease, but are renewed after an interval, with the result that the placenta or afterbirth is separated from the interior of the uterus and passed out to the exterior. Further contractions of the uterus help to close the torn blood vessels. The foetal membranes are passed out with the placenta and the remains of the umbilical cord.

In a normal parturition, the three stages of labor last respectively about eleven hours, one hour, and a quarter of an hour; the birth of the first born takes longer, the three stages taking about sixteen hours, two hours, and a quarter of an hour. At the beginning of labor the pains occur at intervals of about fifteen to thirty minutes; they gradually become much more frequent until they are taking place every two or three minutes. Each contraction lasts from thirty to ninety seconds, but the actual sensation conveyed continues longer. The pressure exerted at each contraction is considerable.

In a typical parturition the head is expelled first, but this is not always so. When twins are born the second child is usually expelled about half an hour after the first, though there may be a considerably longer interval. Usually there is a discharge of blood and mucus from the uterus for about two weeks after parturition, and this varies in amount and duration in different individuals.

Puberty and the Climacteric

The first occurrence of menstruation marks the age of puberty. This normally occurs in girls at from twelve to fifteen, or about a year earlier than puberty in boys, though it may be earlier or later in both sexes.

At puberty ripe ova and spermatozoa are produced for the first time and the sex organs undergo some degree of enlargement. In connection with this change the secondary sexual characters (that is, bodily characters correlated with sex but not directly associated with reproduction) become developed or accentuated. The most important of these are an acceleration of growth; in the boy there is a growth of hair in the pubic region and, later, on the face and other parts of the body. There is an enlargement of the larynx with consequent deepening of the voice, a process which is not completed until about the twenty-fifth year. In the girl the pelvis widens at puberty, and the subcutaneous layer of fat, which assists so largely in giving the body its graceful contour, is deposited. In both sexes there are correlated psychological changes.

The menstrual cycle comes to an end at the menopause or climacteric, at an average age of forty-five. Atrophic changes then take place in the ovaries, uterus, and mammary glands, and ovulation no longer occurs. Sexual desire usually abates, though it may be very marked during the change, and may persist for many years afterward. The changes associated with the climacteric may continue for three to five years, menstruation being at first irregular and then finally ceasing. The organic functions tend to be irregular during the post-cessation stage. Palpitation, dyspepsia, sweating, and frequent flushing of the skin are common, and in a few cases there may be hysteria, neurasthenic symptoms, and, rarely, mental instability. After the change is completed the metabolism or general condition of physiological activity settles down on a new level and the various organs become once more adjusted so as to permit of a normal existence, uninfluenced by sexual or other bodily disturbances.

In the male there is no specific climacteric, sexual capacity usually declining gradually. It is known, however, that spermatozoa may continue to be produced in small numbers even in extreme old age, and that insemination may still be successfully performed, though the chances of a union being sterile are undoubtedly increased. Speaking generally, sexual and reproductive activity in the male is definitely reduced by the age of fifty, but the decline may begin earlier, or it may be postponed till considerably later in particularly virile individuals. This period may be associated with psychological changes, and some derangement of anatomical structure and of physiological function, such as enlargement of the prostate, but the process of sexual decline is often so gradual as to be almost unnoticeable.

III. Man Compared With the Lower Animals

It has been stated that with man there is no season of the year to which sexual activity is restricted, though there is evidence that in temperate climates there is a maximum of conceptions in May, and further, that there is some correlation between temperature (and probably other environmental factors) and the incidence of conception. With man, as with the males of the domestic animals, sperm production proceeds throughout the whole year, there being no period of rut as in so many wild species. In the human female on the other hand, although there is no sexual season of the year, there are, as we have seen, recurrent periods at which the ova are discharged from the ovary. We have seen also that there is evidence that ovulation tends to take place periodically in women with a normal cycle at about the fourteenth day after the beginning of the menstrual flow.

In the domestic animals, as with the vast majority of wild mammalian species, ovulation occurs in association with definite periods of sexual desire known as the periods of heat, or *oestrus,* to which coition is generally restricted. In some species ovulation may take place just after oestrus; in nearly all it is closely associated with it. In women sexual desire is not so restricted, but it is averred that there is a tendency for desire for coition to be greater at about the ovulation periods than at other times. The matter has, however, been obscured by personal, psychological and social influences and possibly also by nutrition, especially under conditions of civilization, and coition occurs quite frequently during pregnancy when it can have no physiological significance. An interesting parallel is to be found in the domestic rabbit, which will also frequently copulate during pregnancy.

The human female is also similar to the females of some of the domestic animals in having a succession of cycles going on throughout the whole year, the menstrual cycle of woman and monkeys corresponding to the short oestrous cycles of the lower mammals. In each case, so far as the ovaries are concerned, the cycle (in the absence of pregnancy) is divisible into two main phases, one, in which certain of the ovarian follicles are large and protruding—a phase which ends at ovulation—and a second phase in which the follicles have given place to the corpora lutea that are formed from them. The second phase corresponds approximately to the uterine stage of growth already referred to, and the first phase to the other three uterine stages.

These comparisons bring us to the consideration of the testis and ovary as organs elaborating internal secretions passed into the circulating blood and controlling the desire and capacity for sexual intercourse and the phases of the sexual cycle.

IV. THE INTERNAL SECRETIONS

A number of organs of the body are known to elaborate chemical substances, now commonly called hormones, some of which are essential for the maintenance of life, and others of lesser importance though performing functions which play a normal part in the economy of the organism. Such endocrine organs, as they are called, include the suprarenal, pituitary, and thyroid glands. The suprarenal produces an important hormone that acts on muscle, and particularly on the muscles of the heart and blood vessels, causing them to contract; it also produces other hormones of uncertain significance. The thyroid elaborates a hormone which is normally essential for life and in particular for growth. When the thyroid enlarges it gives rise to goiter. The functions of the pituitary are discussed below. There are other glands which secrete both through a duct (external secretion) and also into the blood (internal secretion). The pancreas discharges a digestive juice by a duct into the upper gut, but it also produces insulin, this internal secretion being liberated by the pancreatic cells directly into the blood. Without insulin, carbohydrate food material (starch, sugar) cannot be utilized and stored; in fact, it is lost to the organism by being excreted through the kidneys in the form of sugar. Such excretion of sugar in the urine occurs in the disease known as diabetes mellitus.

Most endocrine organs have no particular or special relation to the reproductive system, though they all combine in influencing general bodily activities which in turn affect and condition the sexual and generative processes.

The gonads resemble the pancreas in being endocrine organs that are also provided with ducts; these carry the discharged generative products (ova and spermatozoa) away from the gonad, as we have seen above. That the testes and ovaries are veritably endocrine organs has been recognized in a vague sort of way ever since man carried out the practice of castration, for it has been known from earliest times that the removal of the gonads (or at any rate the testes) exercised a profound effect upon the bodily form and also upon its functional activities.

Castration was practiced on animals for economic reasons, when it was desired to utilize them for other purposes than breeding, and it was recognized that besides arresting the development of the typical male characters it promoted fattening, and in the case of animals used for work rendered them more tractable. It was also practiced on men or boys when it was desired to desex them that they might be employed as eunuchs. On boys it was also done when it was desired that they should retain their treble or soprano voice as choristers.

The effects of testicular removal in man were well known, and it was long ago realized that if the operation were done before puberty it prevented the enlargement of the larynx and the growth of hair on the body and in a general way maintained the juvenile characters, resulting in a type which in many respects resembled the female but which was in reality rather neutral or asexual. Similarly with the female, though ovariotomy (removal of the ovaries) was not practiced nearly so widely as castration of the male, it was known in early days that the operation on animals resulted in the cessation of the oestrous cycle.

The progress of scientific research in the present century made it possible to demonstrate that the egg- and sperm-producing functions of the gonads were something apart from or additional to their endocrine activities, and that the capacity for producing the reproductive cells could be destroyed without interfering with the gonads as endocrine organs. In recent years the results of investigation have gone much further, and substances have been extracted from the gonads which could be injected and to a large extent replace the naturally secreted hormones. The chemical constitution of these substances has been ascertained, and in some cases they have been manufactured in the laboratory. Lastly, there have been prepared synthetic compounds which, although exhibiting some chemical difference from the sex hormones formed in the gonads, yet possess identical or similar effects when administered to the living individual.

All the sex hormones, as well as these artificially produced substances which resemble the sex hormones in their activities, are composed of the three common chemical elements, carbon, hydrogen, and oxygen, and their chemical structure is also, generally speaking, similar, especially in the case of the natural hormones.

Substances having the properties normally ascribed to the male hormones have been isolated from male urine. These are called androsterone and dehydroandrosterone. It is not known where they are produced in the body, but there is a presumption that they are derived from compounds formed in the testes. Substances having the physiological properties of sex hormones have also been obtained from the suprarenal organs. Androsterone and dehydroandrosterone are definitely of the nature of sex hormones, since if injected into castrated animals they stimulate the development of the accessory male glands such as the seminal vesicles, or cause the growth of the secondary sexual characters such as the combs of fowls, it being possible to stimulate the underdeveloped comb of the capon to grow into a comb like that of a cock.

Another hormone having the same physiological properties as the two just mentioned but with a slightly different chemical constitution has been prepared from the testis itself. This is called testosterone. It is far more potent than androsterone or dehydroandrosterone, and it is presumably the natural testicular product which is normally responsible for the growth and development of the accessory male organs (prostatic gland and others) and all the characters and qualities which we are accustomed to associate with maleness, besides being an excitant of sexual desire and regulating all the processes and functions of the male reproductive system.

It is to be noted that whereas the injection into the circulating blood of these substances in recently castrated animals, or animals in a state of sexual rest, will promote the development of the sexual organs and processes and the characteristically male qualities, the taking of them by the mouth is usually ineffective, the hormones being destroyed or acted upon chemically in the alimentary canal before they can be absorbed into the system.

There is one other matter of great importance which may be mentioned here. From what has already been said it is clear that whereas the injection of male hormones can take the place of those produced naturally in the body, so that as long as the injections are maintained the individual can be sexually potent and have normal sexual relations and experience coition, the accessory sexual organs and secondary sexual characters being fully retained, there is nevertheless a condition of complete sterility since there are no organs or structures from which spermatozoa can be produced.

A comparable condition may be brought about in another way. Without castration or the removal of the testes, the spermatozoa and sperm-producing tissue may be completely destroyed, while the hormone-producing tissue or interstitial tissue between the spermatogenetic tubules is left uninjured. This may be effected by radium or X-ray treatment, or the same result may be secured by the simple operation of cutting through the vasa deferentia or spermatic ducts so that spermatozoa can no longer be discharged. Such individuals are rendered completely sterile, but they are not castrated or desexed. They have the normal physical characteristics and instincts of entire individuals.

It has even been claimed that destruction of the sperm-producing tissue, by providing more nourishment or scope for development for the interstitial cells, may actually increase sexual potency (although of course the individual is sterile) and result in some rejuvenation in old age; but there is little real evidence for such a view. The suggestion that rejuvenation may be effected by the grafting of testicular interstitial tissue derived from monkeys or some other animals (the theory of the so-called "monkey gland" as a rejuvenator) is also without much practical basis, if only because attempted grafts are known to survive, at best, for but a short time in the bodies of their hosts.

Just as there is a number of male hormonal substances known to exist naturally and many more which have been prepared, so also there are female hormonal substances, known collectively as oestrins. These include both natural and artificial substances, of varying degrees of potency. As in the case of the male hormones, oestrins are found to be excreted in the urine, presumably in conditions where these substances are waste products and of no use to the organism. The oestrins are in a general way substances which when injected into a female animal which has been castrated or into individuals in a state of sexual rest will produce symptoms of oestrus or heat, so that sexual intercourse may be experienced.

They also promote the development of the typically female characteristics, and tend to change neutral individuals such as female castrates into those with the normal female characteristics of the species. Thus, whereas the removal of the ovaries causes the menstrual or oestrous cycles to cease, or if done prior to puberty prevents the onset of the cycle, the injection and absorption of oestrin may cause the normal manifestations of the cycle. Menstruation and the complete series of cyclical processes have been induced in women whose ovaries had been removed, by successive injections of the appropriate sex hormones.

As in the case of the male, the most potent sex hormones are believed to be produced by the gonad, and there is one called oestradiol, which has been isolated from the ovary and has been thought to represent the true ovarian oestrogenic hormone. It is of far greater potency than any of the sex hormones found elsewhere in the system of the female.

It has been recorded above that the ovarian follicles, after they have discharged their ova, become converted into pigmented yellow bodies known as corpora lutea. These bodies have been shown to discharge important functions, being special ovarian organs of internal secretion and of great importance to the female individual during pregnancy. Indeed, in the absence of a corpus luteum pregnancy cannot take place, and if in women the yellow body is destroyed during the earlier part of pregnancy, the process cannot continue. This is because the corpus luteum is essential for that building up of the uterus which admits of the development and nutrition of the young within that organ. Not only is the corpus luteum necessary for the growth of the uterus but it is also—at any rate normally—essential for the development of the mammary glands which provide nourishment for the infant.

The functional activity of the corpus luteum is now known to be due to the action of a specific hormone, called progesterone. This substance has not only been extracted in a pure form from the corpus luteum but it has also been made artificially from the soya bean. In the absence of the corpus luteum or of the entire ovary (that is, if these be removed some time after the beginning of pregnancy) the injection of progesterone at frequent intervals during pregnancy will maintain the condition and the young may be delivered at the end of the natural term if the injections of the hormone are at that stage discontinued.

If pregnancy in a woman does not take place after ovulation owing to the ovum not being fertilized, the corpus luteum persists only for about three weeks, but it is believed to play a part during this period in building up the uterus preparatory to the next menstrual discharge. In fact the process of menstruation may be regarded as the removal or abortion of something prepared for a fertilized ovum which is not there.

Progesterone is produced by a special part of the ovary, the corpus luteum; oestradiol, on the other hand, is believed to be manufactured by the ovarian follicles or by the ground substance of the ovary. These two ovarian hormones, oestradiol (or at any rate some form of oestrin or female sex hormone) and progesterone are in part at least normally responsible for the two main phases of the menstrual cycle already described. Moreover, this natural two-phase variation can be imitated in women deprived of their ovaries by appropriate injections of oestradiol and progesterone.

In animals which do not have a menstrual cycle and which enter into a state of sexual rest for a part of the year (the nonbreeding season) the female sex hormone is believed to be produced in much reduced quantities at such times of nonactivity.

The pituitary body is a small gland lying just beneath the brain, with which it is connected by a stalk. It consists of two lobes, anterior and posterior, and both of these are organs of internal secretion. Some of the hormones they produce have a direct functional connection with the reproductive organs.

The posterior lobe of the pituitary manufactures a substance called pituitrin which has been extracted from it. What its precise functions are in the living animal is not clearly known, but under experimental conditions it can be shown to act powerfully upon the muscles of the uterus. Thus, pituitrin can have a valuable medical application in expediting parturition and the delivery of the child, for when injected in small quantities and with due precautions into the blood of a woman or female animal at the time when pregnancy should terminate, it helps the uterine muscles to contract and so assists in the expulsion of the young. Pituitrin may be used in difficult cases where the unassisted power of contraction on the part of the womb is inadequate for bringing about birth.

The anterior lobe of the pituitary, although contiguous with the posterior lobe, is a separate ductless gland. Minute as it is (it is only about as big as a pea) it apparently produces several hormones which act upon the other organs of internal secretion. It is an important factor in growth and in this respect seems to act somewhat similarly to the thyroid. It is now known also to produce one and probably two hormones which act directly upon the gonads, both in the male and in the female.

That there was a functional correlation between the anterior pituitary and the sex organs had long been known to clinical workers, and sterility and various abnormal conditions and aberrations on the part of these organs have been found to be associated with abnormally high or low pituitary secretion. A condition of adiposity associated with delay in the development of the sexual organs and characters is a result of anterior pituitary deficiency. Such a condition is seen in "fat boys" like the one described by Dickens in the "Pickwick Papers."

There may be all gradations of pituitary deficiency or excess, and the "fat boy" condition is often transient, being succeeded later by normality.

The functional correlation between the anterior pituitary and the sexual organs has been established experimentally. The injections of particular substances obtained from the anterior pituitary have been shown in animals to promote sexual development, to increase the number of eggs produced, and so to promote fertility; and in general to control and be a necessary factor in the sexual cycle. Another substance extracted from the pituitary can be made to stimulate the growth of the luteal tissue of the ovaries.

It is supposed, therefore, that there are two anterior pituitary hormones acting on the sex organs, one of which promotes the development of the gametes (ova and spermatozoa) and the tissues in which they develop, and another which is functional only in the female, stimulating the growth of the corpora lutea and regulating the luteal phase of the cycle. Moreover, further substances have been extracted from the anterior pituitary which stimulate the growth of the mammary glands or cause them to secrete milk. Lastly, it is definitely established that in the absence of the anterior pituitary the gonads of the young fail to develop and in the adult undergo atrophy.

A substance similar to but probably not identical with this anterior pituitary hormone has been extracted from the blood, the placenta and the urine of pregnant women; and its presence in the urine is regarded as a diagnostic sign of pregnancy. It has been thought to be produced in the placenta. The chemical composition has not been determined for any of the anterior pituitarylike principles.

The anterior pituitary in its relation to the genital organs has, further, an important function of a more special kind in so far as it serves as a regulator, bringing the reproductive processes into general harmony with surrounding conditions and in particular with seasonal ones and those depending on the relations of the sexes and those between the mother and her offspring. The evidence shows very clearly that it is through the anterior pituitary that nervous messages of very varied kinds are transmitted to the gonads. These nervous messages may arise in any of the organs of sight, hearing, smell or the different kinds of organs of feeling. The stimuli received in any of these ways are conducted along the correlated nerves to the brain, which transmits them to the pituitary. The latter, in response to stimuli, secretes hormones which in turn act upon the gonads—testes or ovaries, as the case may be.

This, stated in summarized form, is the chief way in which the reproductive organs are believed to be brought into relation with external events, and in which the individual human being or animal is sexually affected by outside change whether induced by the physical environment, or by the contiguity of other individuals and more particularly those of the opposite sex. It must, however, always be borne in mind that the genital system, like the other systems of the body, is necessarily conditioned by the environment and that it could not function without being supplied with the necessary food, oxygen and other constituents which are essential for the proper working of the whole body.

The anterior pituitary gland, then, is a regulator of sexual function. It receives nervous messages through the brain from the environment without and transmits them by means of hormones secreted into the circulating blood to the reproductive organs within. The stimuli received and transmitted in this way are known technically as being "exteroceptive." We may now consider some of the more important of these exteroceptive factors which control the incidence of the sexual season in animals and the activities of the reproductive functions.

V. EXTEROCEPTIVE FACTORS IN SEXUAL CHANGE

It has been shown experimentally with many of the lower mammals as well as with birds, amphibians and fish that light may be an important exteroceptive factor in inducing reproductive activity. This result is in agreement with the generally observed fact that most wild animals have their breeding seasons in the spring and early summer when the daylight is increasing. There is the further fact that when animals are transferred to the southern hemisphere they rapidly adjust themselves to the local conditions, which in the matter of light are in actual time the reverse of what they are in the north. Thus, in many animals, both species and individuals, the time for the breeding may be reversed after the crossing of the equator. In a similar way in a particular species of animal or bird reproductive activity can be induced experimentally in what is normally the nonbreeding season by having recourse to the use of artificial light during part of the night. Furthermore, it has been shown experimentally that light has no influence upon the sexual cycle or the activity of the breeding organs if the pituitary be removed, and there is every evidence that the light stimulus is transmitted through the intermediation of that particular endocrine organ. As to whether sexual activity in man is influenced by the exteroceptive action of light there is no direct evidence, but there is a presumption that such may be the case.

We may now consider those exteroceptive stimuli which, arising from the relations of the sexes, may be a factor in the onset of breeding and modify the phases of the sexual cycle. A very clear example of this kind of phenomenon is shown by some of the lower mammals, such as the rabbit and the ferret, which normally only discharge the eggs from the ovaries as a result of sexual intercourse. This is a special device to induce a proper synchronization in the presence of both kinds of gametes (spermatozoa and ova) in the female reproductive tract so as to increase the chances of successful fertilization, and consequently of pregnancy. If owing to some mischance, such as the fertilized ova not becoming attached, the ovaries and other genital organs enter into a condition of "pseudopregnancy," the discharged follicles of the ovaries are transformed into corpora lutea just as they are during true pregnancy. The mammary glands also undergo growth and eventually secrete milk in spite of the fact that the rabbit or other animal has not become pregnant.

This condition of pseudopregnancy in the rabbit, ferret, and some other animals can be induced under certain circumstances notwithstanding that actual sexual intercourse may not have occurred. Moreover, it can be brought about experimentally as a result of ovulation either by injection of a hormone obtained from the anterior pituitary or by electrical stimulation of the brain or spinal cord. It is thus shown that the incidence of the sexual periods can be modified by nervous stimuli of various kinds and that they act through the intermediation of the brain and the anterior pituitary gland. In the absence of this latter organ the results are not brought about.

In birds more than in mammals the discharge of the eggs from the ovary occurs as a result of a stimulus derived from the male, though this is not the case with the domestic fowl, the pheasant and similar birds. With most species of birds, unmated females will not usually lay eggs, but with both birds and some species of mammals the presence of another female may sometimes provoke sufficient stimulus to cause the discharge of the eggs, which in the case of the birds pass out fully formed to the exterior in the process of laying.

The evidence shows very clearly that the anterior pituitary gland is an organ which has, as one of its most important functions, the effective synchronization of the male and female sexual processes, which are so co-ordinated as to admit of the fertilization of the ova of the female by the spermatozoa of the male. We are thus brought to an understanding of the physiological use and meaning of the sexual display presented by most birds and a large number of other animals, as well as of all courtship phenomena shown by so many of the higher forms of life, including man. The anterior pituitary serves as an intermediary for mutual stimulation and thereby provides a means by which the two sexes are brought simultaneously into a condition for successful procreation.

Not only sexual posturing or bodily adornment but any kind of stimulus arising from the presence of the opposite sex acts exteroceptively upon the brain and thence upon the pituitary of the individual stimulated, and the pituitary in turn sends out hormones or chemical messengers to the genital organs. It follows that mutual pituitary stimulation due to the contiguity of the male and female individuals promotes the growth and functional activity of testes and ovaries alike and is consequently a matter of great importance for the fertility of the race.

VI. Fertility and Sterility

It is fitting to conclude this short account of the physiology of reproduction with a few remarks on the causes of fertility and sterility. The latter condition may of course be due to disease or to some malformation or abnormal state of one or other of the genital organs. Such abnormal or pathological causes are outside the scope of the present work. But, apart from sterility due to disease, a reduction in fertility may be the consequence of physiological factors the effects of which may often be prevented from operating or whose influence may be reduced.

Pregnancy in a woman or in an animal is the result of the union of a single spermatozoon with a single ovum, or in the case of twin or multiple births of a corresponding number of spermatozoa and ova. In women as a general rule only one ovum is discharged at a time (though twins and triplets are not very uncommon), so that usually of the millions of spermatozoa discharged by the male and entering the female reproductive passages, only one spermatozoon is successful in fertilizing an egg.

In spite of the very large number of spermatozoa discharged it occasionally happens that not a single active sperm reaches the ovum in its passage down the oviduct. Great numbers of spermatozoa must in any case lose their way and perish in the glands of the uterus or elsewhere in the female reproductive tract; the enormous number of spermatozoa produced is nature's device to increase the chances that the ovum shall be fertilized by one of them. There is always the possibility (though it is not a very common one), that where a couple fail to have children it is not the female partner but the male who is responsible owing to an inadequacy in the supply of healthy spermatozoa.

A common cause of temporary sterility operates in cases where sexual intercourse is practiced at unsuitable times. It has already been said that whereas no time in the menstrual cycle of the woman can be regarded as an absolutely "safe period" (that is, a season when coition will inevitably be succeeded by sterility), there is evidence that intercourse is most likely to result in conception if performed about the fourteenth or fifteenth day after the beginning of the menstrual flow, since ovulation is more frequent at this season than at any other stage of the cycle.

A question of considerable practical importance relates to the possibility that the female orgasm, that is, the climax of sensation at coition, may be a factor in human ovulation in the same kind of way that coition is an essential factor for ovulation in the rabbit and the ferret. There is no doubt that the intensity of sensation accompanying the female orgasm is very variable, and that with some women coition may occur without full sexual satisfaction, the orgasm being only imperfectly completed. It is possible in such cases where there may be some degree of incompatibility between the two partners in coition that ovulation may fail to take place. Cases have been recorded where a woman married to one husband may never experience a true orgasm and fail to have children, and subsequently after union with another husband may experience the orgasm the first time and produce offspring. It must not be supposed that the orgasm is normally essential for fertility, but it may be regarded as extremely probable that failure in mutual pituitary stimulation due to the absence of any sort of courtship phenomena is a cause of temporary or permanent sterility with married couples. The orgasm also probably plays a part in the sexual act by leading to contraction and relaxation of the womb and thus to a sort of suction of the spermatic fluid upward into the genital canal.

Another cause of temporary, or, occasionally even of permanent, sterility in both male and female, is a condition of excessive fatness or adiposity. This is a frequent cause in domestic animals, and it undoubtedly operates, though to a much less extent, in men and women. In the lower mammals it is known that the ovarian follicles degenerate as a result of excessive adiposity. The smaller and least mature follicles are affected less than the larger or more ripe ones, and if the condition of fatness is reduced the former may take the place of the degenerate follicles and normality be restored. Reduced fertility leading to complete sterility may, on the other hand, result from too impoverished a condition and malnutrition due to underfeeding or a faulty and unsatisfactory diet is known to be a cause of ovarian follicular degeneration in animals. An improvement in the quantity and quality of the food is followed by maturation of those follicles which have not perished and by a recovery of fertility. This is in the female. Sterility due to impoverishment of nutrition is rarer in the male, and may be said to occur only in extreme cases of underfeeding. How far these influences operate in the case of man is unknown. It is, however, well established that infertility in woman is in many cases due to a diminution in the normal activity of the sex glands and the sex hormones. In some cases this is accompanied by abnormality in the menstrual process. It has been shown experimentally in animals that failure on the part of the male to produce spermatozoa and failure on the part of the female to maintain development of the embryo in the uterus can be due to the absence of a particular accessory food substance known to scientists as Vitamin E. This food substance exists normally in green food, wheat germ, and so on, and is present in all normal diets. An animal such as a rat if deprived of Vitamin E, although it may be maintained in a state of health so far as its other functions are concerned is unable to have young. As to whether the absence or scarcity of Vitamin E is ever responsible for infertility in men and women is unknown. But it is unlikely that it is a factor in conditions approaching normality.

7.
The Meaning of Fatherhood

by *Therese Benedek, M. D.*

The child has been called "the father of the man." In the same sense, the personality of the parent may be profoundly influenced by the feelings he has for his child. The elements of self-reference involved in fatherhood are brilliantly explored in this paper written expressly for this volume by the author of *Insight and Personality Adjustment and Psychosexual Functions in Women*. Dr. Benedek is a Staff Member of the Institute for Psychoanalysis, Chicago.

See also Chapter 7 in Women: "Some Problems of Motherhood."

Parenthood

PARENTHOOD DOES NOT MEAN the fulfillment of a biological function only, that of begetting and bearing children; it also implies the principal social function of the adult individual. Biology defines the role that male and female invariably play in propagation of the species. The need, however, that man and woman have for each other in and for fulfillment of this function represents the roots out of which social organizations grow. The long-lasting dependence of the human offspring represents a biological demand on the mother for nursing and care; this, in turn, is the source of woman's need for support and protection by the man who is usually the father of her child or children. These relatively "simple" biological facts form the basis of the primary social organization: the family. Its function is to safeguard the physical growth and emotional development of the child.

Until the last decade of the nineteenth century, science had not scrutinized the emotional processes by which the family functions. Then psychoanalysis discovered the subtle psychic processes by which the individual, growing up in a family, incorporates within himself the cultural patterns of that society of which the family is a part. This means that in developing toward sexual maturity the individual incorporates within his own emotional life the ideals and conflicts that are associated with parenthood in general as well as those that have been transmitted to him (and to her) through the interpersonal relationship between the particular child and his or her parents. Although this learning, which becomes an intrinsic part of one's "mental apparatus," of one's self, occurs unconsciously, nowadays many young men and women are working arduously at becoming "adequate" parents.

"Adequate"—how modest an adjective this is, although it is used so often in our modern sociologic and psychiatric studies of parents, in comparison to the idealized concepts that pervaded the illusions of the patriarchal family. One does not need to review history very far to realize the shifts and changes that have occurred in our fast-moving civilization even to such an everlasting institution as the family. Most middle-aged Americans and many of the younger ones as well were raised in the puritan tradition of the patriarchal family.

The emotional structure of such a family appeared to be unchangeably set. Its main representative, the father-husband, was assumed to be strong, active, providing for his wife and children not only a livelihood but also the means of emotional security. In return, his authority was not questioned; his own goals and aims were the goals and aims of his children. His wife, linked to her husband in a lasting marriage, derived her emotional security not only from her husband, but even more from and through her children. Bearing them without questioning the laws of nature, she raised them in the security of their love, appreciation, and gratefulness to her. The children, in turn, accepted parental authority with devotion and gratefulness (or, at least, were expected to do so). Having incorporated firm ideals (one might say, rigid ideals) of parenthood, the same children, when fully grown, acted according to those ideals; that is, they accepted their function of parenthood with the same hopes and expectations, with the same responsibilities and ideals as their own parents once did.

This, of course, is an extreme generalization that omits the conflicts and struggles that are involved in the development of each individual and that were also effective in the patriarchal family[1] which aimed to transmit the well-established patterns of a relatively homogeneous and almost repetitious developmental goal.

The function of the family is, no doubt, more complex in our present democratic, individualistic society. The ideal of our society is marriage between equal partners; the goal of such a marriage is the pursuit of happiness through continual individual maturation of each of the partners. We assume that the family, founded on equal privileges and responsibilities for the marital partners, appears to be best ordained to transmit to the children the requirements of our culture: a more complete individuation. Thus children are raised not with the ideal of becoming the image of their parents but each as an individual in his own right. At the same time and in the

---

[1] The clinical manifestations of these emotional struggles led Freud to discover the development of the personality and its "controls" such as superego, conscience.

same environment, each must acquire for himself as an individual the capacity to adjust himself to the requirements of marriage and parenthood when his own time comes. No doubt, young parents today start out on an almost uncharted course to raise children toward an unknown goal in an insecure world.

All this must be said before parenthood can be separated into its biological components of fatherhood and motherhood, since parenthood as an experience is a continual emotional interaction between mother—father—child. This dynamic unit, the family triangle, has always existed, albeit, it has been expressed by different patterns of behavior in different cultures. The father's psychodynamic function in this triangle has often been disguised (as in the patriarchal family); it has even been eliminated in varying degrees. In the family structure of our current culture, however, the father's role in the family triangle becomes more and more obvious. Fatherhood, in the current family structure, more than ever before, besides being a biological function, is an emotional (*i.e.*, a psychodynamic and sociodynamic) function par excellence.

Fatherhood

Since nature connects paternity with the gratification of the sexual urge, the emotional factors involved in fatherhood have seldom been analyzed. While the word *motherhood* sounds familiar, its complement *fatherhood* appears almost strange and new. Yet there are emotional (instinctive and social) trends integrated in the experience of fatherhood that complement those that find expression in motherhood.

Sexual maturity does not only mean the readiness of the genital apparatus to fulfill its function in procreation; it also means that the individual has learned to reconcile his sexual needs with his conscience. This implies that he has developed a personality that, on the one hand, can accept and enjoy sexuality and, on the other, is able to adjust the gratifications of his sexual needs to the external demands of society. Sexual maturation thus supplies the motivation for further development of the individual that is achieved in marriage and through parenthood. From the point of view of the personality, the aim of maturation—the acculturation of the sexual drive—is the same in both sexes. But in regard to its biological goal, *the sexual drive is organized differently in man and woman in order to serve specific functions in procreation.*

The propagative function of the male, under the control of one group of gonadal hormones, the androgens, is discharged in a single act of cohabitation. Since paternity depends on one act, the motivation for which is experienced as a compelling desire for orgastic discharge of a tension, one might ask the question, "Is there a genuine instinctual urge for fatherhood?" Or, "Is fatherhood primarily a social accomplishment that takes advantage of the sexual need to induce man to assume responsibility for his offspring?"

Propagation can be considered a special manifestation of growth. The individual, after having achieved maturity, surpasses the growth of his own body in his germ cells, through which he produces a new individual. Man's desire to survive in the offspring of his own sex is documented by rites and religions, by customs and socioeconomic organizations. Thus even in the civilization of today, so proud of the achievement of "equality of the sexes," there are many motivations for the almost universal preference for a male child. Among these, society's

higher evaluation of the male sex, although it is always
kept in the foreground, appears actually to be only secondary and a result of the biological motivation of parenthood in the male. This primarily is intended for the
continuation of the self and therefore can be satisfied
directly only by a child of the father's sex. It is of no
avail to try to deny the father's overflowing gratification
if his newborn child is a son, or to attempt to minimize
the emotional adjustment that is necessary if it is a
daughter.

These aspects of fatherhood hardly answer the question of whether or not there exists in man a primary,
biological tendency toward becoming and being a provider. No doubt, nature left it to the female to bear the
young, to protect and feed them, even to teach them
certain skills in securing food and surviving. Yet there
are exceptions throughout the animal world, especially
among birds and fish.[2] While it would be definitely exaggerated to assume that animals live in families (as
humans do), observations show that mammalian males
also (for example, chimpanzee fathers) take over the
care of an infant if the mother is incapacitated or rejects
the child. It is beyond the scope of this article to trace
the tendency in the human male to provide for the wife
and children to its biologic and emotional origin. Let it
suffice to say that one of the origins of this tendency is
the biological bisexuality, but probably more important
is the experience of biological dependency on the mother.
Men too are born and nursed by their mothers; each
man's earliest security as well as his earliest orientation in
this world were conveyed to him by his mother and has
been "learned" by him through identification with her.

[2]Burns, Eugene. *The Sex Life of Wild Animals.* Rinehart & Co.,
New York, 1953.

In the development of man the early emotional dependence on and identification with the mother is overcome step by step through the developmental identifications with the father. This development is often fraught with conflicts and anxieties since our civilization expects man to deny and repress every manifestation of his emotional dependency that is considered contradictory to his virility and therefore is in conflict with all his ego aspirations. The same cultural environment that has set such rigid standards against emotional bisexuality is maintained by an economic system that separates the function of "providing" from its emotional roots. Geographically as well as in other ways, man is separated from his family, from the experience of the emotional interchange in being the provider for family, for wife and children. It is not our task here to discuss how industrial civilization affected isolation between the two biological (emotional) aspects of procreation in man nor to elaborate the effects that such isolation has had upon his emotional household. This is mentioned only to indicate that socio-economic factors are responsible for the fact that the links between the two aspects of the procreative function, sexual cohabitation and providing for wife and offspring, are often unrecognizably disguised. Yet under conditions that impede the reproductive function, such as sterility of either of the marital partners, or by enforced separation, man's instinct for survival in his offspring becomes urgent and therefore accessible to analysis. The great experiment, the war, which threatened the survival of man, exposed the instinctual motivations of fatherhood in a large number of individuals.[3]

In our age of "planned parenthood" we have reason

[3] Benedek, Therese. *Insight and Personality Adjustment.* Ronald Press Company, New York, 1946.

to be surprised by the increased birth rate during the war since the external circumstances of war in our society would seem to interfere with the natural urge for parenthood. The father-to-be knows that he will not be able to help his wife during the pregnancy; he will not share her worries or her elation; he will not be able to see his baby perhaps for months or years, if ever. Yet he is deeply happy in being able to go away with the feeling that his life will be continued, that he has created a tie that gives him a sense of duty and aspiration to life. He is almost consciously aware that he uses this fact of survival in his child as a means to increase the chances of his own survival; it helps him to overcome hardships and deprivations. This indicates that the trauma of separation increases the man's dependence upon all his existing relationships; it activates and deepens the need for his wife's love (as well as for his mother's). These dependent needs may be in conflict with his ego aspirations; he would lose self-esteem were he to recognize his regressive tendencies. In his conscious desire for procreation, however, he overcomes through his virility these regressive trends. While he achieves gratification in love, he reassures himself of his masculinity, thus elevating himself above his fears. At the same time he pledges to his wife his willingness to take on responsibilities, thus creating in his child the representation of his maturity. When man fears that his survival is threatened, his desire for reproduction becomes a process of reparation, a means of overcoming anxiety. The psychology of fatherhood can be best presented by pointing out its two main roots: one, the urge to conquer man's dependence by love and, two, to fulfill man's desire to become like his father.

With the act of reproduction he not only asserts his

biological function, he also achieves an ambition active since his early childhood—his competition with his father. This competition is the manifestation of the biological tendency to develop to masculine maturity. During the process of growth it had many phases and aspects; sometimes it was repressed with fear; other times it was emphasized with pride. When he gives a child to his wife, he not only conquers his fears but he also reaches a new level of integration in his personality. While he himself has become a link in the chain of the generations between his father and his child, he has built another rung on the ladder to his own psychosexual maturity.

The emotional relationship between father and child proceeds on two levels; one is the father's identification with his child and the other is the father's identification with his own father. Expressed in terms of these identifications, the emotional needs and gratifications of fatherhood can be easily understood. Not all aspects of these identifications come to the fore simultaneously and with the same intensity.

The personality of the father as well as external circumstances will influence the emotional manifestations of his *fatherliness*. Whatever the instinctual roots of fatherhood are, until it becomes the emotional relationship of the father to his child, fatherliness draws on various emotional resources that have been molded by the various influences during the development of the individual.

Psychoanalysis tells us more about the developmental processes of becoming a father than of the experiences of being one. Yet in societies where the organization of the family affords the development of the family triangle, the psychodynamic processes of fatherhood are similar to that of motherhood. The father, like the mother, tends

to identify himself with his child; he too repeats unconsciously (through identification and projection) the steps
of his own aspirations and hopes in order to achieve completion of his own personality through his child, through
his children. This is, of course, a generalization and a happy one. However, one should not forget that such intrinsic
dynamic interaction—the family triangle—develops between parents and each of their children separately and
with varying emotional content. Through one child the
parent might experience the resolution of his own conflict and through another he might become keenly aware
of his own weakness. This is not an easy task for the
parent, but it seems that parents, now more than before,
must accept the fact that they will learn and develop to
their full maturation through their children. While in
previous generations the father (for that matter, even
the mother) "knew it all" and "knew it better" and the
parents led the children, who followed without question,
now the reciprocal interaction between parents and children is becoming more and more evident. Sometimes it
seems that the links between the generations were
loosened or even broken through these changes in the
attitudes between parents and children. However, it is
more probable that this articulate and many-sided struggle between the generations indicates that fatherhood
(and motherhood) are progressing beyond their biological function toward their cultural aim: that of higher
individuation.

8.
Sex Psychology of the Unmarried Adult

by Ernest R. Graves

Only in recent years has the problem posed by the unnatural postponement of marriage beyond the age of sexual maturity been lifted out of a limbo of feigned ignorance. The risks to personality inherent in the compromises demanded by our cultural standards are analyzed by an eminent social scientist who, in several books and as Professor of Sociology at the University of North Carolina, was an early exponent of rational education for marriage and family life. Reprinted from *The Sex Life of the Unmarried Adult*, edited by Ira S. Wile, M.D., copyright, 1934, by Vanguard Press, Inc., by permission of the publisher.

See also Chapter 8 in *Women: "The Unmarried."*

IF BY IGNORING A PROBLEM we could destroy it, there would be little sex life before marriage. Even yet, it is orthodox to consider sex a docile impulse that observes the social proprieties and makes appearance only when the man and the woman have crossed the barrier into matrimony. Any premarriage expression is unnatural, menacing, a behavior problem. We have gone so far in the recent past as to expect the boy and the girl to make the passage of puberty, with all its body changes, without becoming conscious of its sex meaning. The veil that taboo has spread over the sex life of the unmarried has been so thick that it has concealed the experience of all except those who have been considered problem persons. That society has ever been committed to such an imposture reveals more than anything else how large a problem sex before marriage has been.

Of late the curtain has been torn. The comfortable assumption that sex can be kept quiescent until marriage invites it to come forth, is at an end. Instead, we find facing us some stubborn and uncomfortable facts once we permit the investigation that prejudice has so long blocked.

The evidences of the sex problems of the unmarried have ever been near the surface. Now that the myth of the nonsex career has been exploded, we are beginning to see why there is a problem and why it is so troublesome. Body maturity runs way ahead of marriage opportunity, so that normally the body is ready for adult sex experience years before men and women are ready for matrimony, according to the prevailing standards of culture. This is not all. Physical sex itself is discordant. As a pleasure-giving impulse, the adolescent sex changes come to maturity sooner than they do as a reproduction function. This division lifts the human sex life out of that of the animal by giving opportunity for psychic enlargement but, at the same time, it becomes an inevitable source of stress.

More trouble comes because those who are thrown into the pubescent upheaval have seldom been prepared for the ordeal forced upon them. Even now, when many parents are beginning to realize the trial of the adolescent, the great majority of children are given no inkling as to the meaning of what is happening to them, and they wrestle with forces that seem to have arisen in the night and without warning. Although sex is presented before the eyes of youth by the movies and other commercial enterprises and used as an exploiting motive, it is only in the rare family that any considerable effort is made to handle the sex problems of the growing child intelligently, frankly, and without any emotion or deception. It would not matter if there were some other way of getting the information and the attitudes which provide favorable passage through adolescence, but the failure of church and school is generally just as great as that of the parent.

For many older youths, particularly young women, trouble comes from another quarter, and this constitutes one of the most pressing of all the vexations of premarriage experience. There is no certainty in the vast majority of cases that the individual will finally pass out of the single life and enter upon marriage. However strong the individual's expectations, however optimistic the hope of finding a life-mate may be, there is always a lingering shadow of doubt, an uncertainty that cannot be pushed aside. It would be one thing for young women to struggle through the temporary testing if there were assurance of its ending in marriage, but only optimists having extraordinary recklessness or good fortune can feel sure that they will marry when they are ready, and only then if they are not too exacting in their choice.

As science pushes forward and gains in its conquest of knowledge of human experience, the significance of sex both before and after marriage constantly increases. We are amazed at the extent to which it is spread through the tissue of personality and the depth to which it is planted in the character. The secretions that pour forth from the testicles and ovaries have an essential part in the endocrine symphony and their contribution is far more complex than the sexual aspects of reproduction ever indicate. Recent discoveries relating to these chemical processes of the body are revolutionizing medical practice as did the investigations of Pasteur, and all of them emphasize the importance of the role of physiological sex for both the man and the woman.

Meanwhile, from a different source, comes another insistence that sex has a larger meaning for the human career than appears on the surface. Our increasing knowledge of this greater significance of sex we owe chiefly to the original explorations of Sigmund Freud and their stimulating effect upon both his disciples and his critics. The psychiatrist and the psychologist, divided though both of them are into groups that differ in their interpretation of sex, unite in affirming that it has a causal influence on human conduct beyond anything ever conceived in the past. Instead of it being, as was once supposed, only the licentious or the abnormal who bring sex into overt expression before marriage, we are forced to recognize the fact, staring at us from all directions, that from birth onward sex plays an active role continuously through life and never accepts expulsion. Not only is there never a time when sex is quiescent; it always refuses to be passive. The crossing, which in the past has been thought of as the time and method of bringing sex into activity, is a purely social boundary which the body does not recognize—an attempt at the regulation of sex for purposes that are larger than the impulses of the individual.

From this point of view, sex development is irregular, with personal differences of tension and with periods of special stress, but always it is a never-ending struggle for integration, not ended by marriage but given a different form. Within or without matrimony sex impulse craves satisfaction, a completeness, a fulfillment, and requires a discipline which makes it an epitome of human life itself. The tendency to elude the human grasp is one of the marked characteristics of our existence. Sex has this same everlasting groping, this quenchless craving, this restless turning to the future. At best, marriage can only soften the discord of conflicting motives and tone down the aggressiveness of adolescent expectation. Marriage, however, as the supremely intimate, complementary experience, leads away from this adolescent stress toward a maturity and a fellowship that mitigates all forms of struggle, whatever their origin.

We are too prone to dissociate the sex career of the individual and to think of it as chiefly an adjustment of one person to another in the fellowship of marriage. Only in narrow and deceptive terms can it be so conceived. We arbitrarily minimize the sex character of pre-marriage associations through motives similar to those that led our parents to ignore the existence of sex problems of children and adolescents.

A great part of the sex life of the unmarried is beneath the surface, and if it rises to consciousness it is in such form that the source from which the influences flow forth escapes attention. It is because of this concealment that there has been until of late the widespread notion that sex means little to the unmarried except when it becomes a conscious physical urge. On the contrary, we now know that traits that appear in the spinster or the bachelor, however distant they may seem from sex, are often the coming out of sexual reactions and conflicts that had their beginning as far back as infancy or early childhood. Even for those married and happily adjusted there is a large number of psychic and physical incitements that are sexual in their origin but are not so interpreted by the persons whom they affect. Both in our changing moods and in our inconsistent emotions there are derivatives of sex.

There has been a disposition in the past to regard sex as essentially reproduction and to insist that its advent is at puberty. By squeezing sex into so narrow an inter-

pretation a great part of its effect upon the unmarried
was covered up. Even when the virgin has no thought of
physical sex and no sublimating of it through a love-
fixation, there are both body and psychic impulses born
of sex equipment and sex desire that operate upon the
emotions and influence the behavior. There is no need
of a Freud to demonstrate that personality is saturated
with sex from the early days of childhood to the very
end of life. Its expression is inevitable but cumulative.
After the individual has crossed into puberty no life
program, no conspiracy of silence, can shut it out, although it is not difficult for the young man or woman
to refuse to admit its presence or to deal with it openly.

No small part of the stress that the unmarried experience on account of the surging of sex impulse is due to
the general unwillingness of the social code to recognize
this premarriage significance of sex desire, at least so far
as the woman is concerned. As we shall see, changes are
taking place, but the pervading and controlling notion
still carries the suggestion that sex before marriage is a
faulty breaking out of impulses that should be so tamed,
that is, so suppressed, as not to constitute any serious
problem in the well-adjusted.

Because this attitude adds to the difficulties of American youth, it must not be inferred that those who,
through exceptionally early training or from adolescent
sophistication, are thoroughly acquainted with the
strength and normality of their sex impulses are entirely
free from any tension. It proves an advantage for sex to
be out in the open, but there still remains the task of
adjusting either to the orthodox social code or to a self-
made, consistent program of conduct. The frequency and
the tenseness of this type of conflict must not betray us
into thinking that all adolescent struggle takes this form

or is of sex origin. The career of adolescence, through the interaction of the individual and the group, provides many occasions for tension, and sometimes even those brought about by social circumstances find a sex expression.

It might seem that no American young person, when sex flares forth from every direction, could possibly escape coming to know the personal impulses that thrust themselves into consciousness as a result of the outer social, or the inner body sex-stimulations, or both working together. It is indeed strange that anyone can avoid the environmental awakening of consciousness of sex when the physical and psychic preparedness for this experience is so thoroughly established. Yet this happens. The observing person does not need to go far afield to find evidence of such extraordinary blindness to the forces operating. The mind has been made so resistant through early teaching that, although the barrier against the penetration of sex is thinner than paper and of no protection, there is complete anesthesia so far as the significance of sex awakening is concerned, an utter absence of frank attention to what is taking place.

This obtuseness to a very significant, and possibly the most compelling part of the individual's life, uncovers the length to which conditioning of sex may go and the sensitiveness sex normally has in childhood to adult pressure. Through such extreme illustrations we come to see that society is chiefly responsible for the premarriage sex tension of youth. This realization of the origin of the strain does not solve the problems of life for either the child, the unmarried adolescent, the unmarried adult, or those in process of domestic adjustment. Since much of this coercion of early sex that causes conflict is inherent in civilization itself, it cannot be erased unless man is stripped of much of his cultural possessions. This fact does not forbid a more rational program, but only the unthinking optimist supposes that the wisest, most scientific of sex education connotes the entire elimination of the stress which those who pass through puberty encounter in one form or another.

The humanizing process which has taken man so far away from his animal origin has extended and refined the sex impulse which originally was so closely tied to reproduction and so thoroughly subservient to it. This spread has increased the opportunities of sex stimulation. Meanwhile, there has been an exploiting of the opportunity that this provides for entrance into the inner life of individuals through suggestions that in subtle or crude form are essentially sexual in character. These suggestions as they are used in modern life to motivate action are often so diluted as not to seem related to sex until they are given a thoroughgoing analysis. As modern men and women have grown more open to sex stimulation there has been corresponding development in the skillful use of this appeal through such popular mediums as, for example, illustrated advertising and the movies. It is because of this that civilization in these days seems so highly sexed.

The transference of physical sex energy to psychic expression so often takes place and is so readily accomplished that it seems to be a symptomatic feature of modern life. It is least apparent in the peasant Negroes of the South, who, by their lack of inhibition of physical sex, are little troubled by tension. They obtain their escape at the cost of arresting their sex life on the plane of meager content.

The ease with which stimulations on the physical level come out in psychic derivatives hides the extent of the

sex life of the unmarried. The unexpected recoil of some
men or women from a fellowship which has been accepted as an erotic substitute for body impulses, when
this intimacy has led to the stimulating of physical desire, reveals that emotions may move in either direction.
The transference from friendship to passion is made so
rapidly and so completely that many a young man or
young woman is forced without warning to a disturbing
self-discovery and for the first time comes to feel the
strength of a sex drive that is both physical and psychic.

There is no standard sex career before marriage and
no safe generalization which assumes a norm in either
the strength or the spread of sex impulse. We find variation both among the married and the unmarried. People range from an apparent frigidity to a sex dominance
that strangles every other impulse. These two radical
variations may be regarded as abnormal. Between them
there appears a distribution of conscious sex drive from
almost utter absence to intense vigor. It must be remembered that this curve represents the suppression or the
awareness of sex rather than its absence or presence. Sex
may meet with such strength of resistance, established
and developed from childhood, that it remains hidden
not only from others but from the individual himself.
It is so thoroughly buried that it seems to have disappeared. It flows, however, underneath, much as does
water beneath the earth's surface. Those individuals who
seem to be devoid of the sex urge are usually less free
and consistent than appears to the observer. Rarely are
they without their problems; they merely have transferred sex from its legitimate field of expression to some
psychic trait where it remains unrecognized. We may
discover flaws in a personality, but because they have no
apparent connection with sex we may not realize their

origin but assume instead that the sex impulse has failed to develop or that during the child's early impressionable period it was strangled.

In addition to the personal differences which are as great as in any feature common to humanity, we need also to keep in mind the effect of age, which also has its personal curve of distribution. At the onset of puberty, for example, in the boy and the girl we detect evidences of the new physiological awakening and disturbance of the body, and, accompanying this under normal circumstances, the beginning of heterosexual attraction. The content of sex experience, in spite of rapid change in the body and the new tension, is meager. It accumulates meaning as maturity proceeds. Here we encounter the dilemma that seems likely always to challenge youth. If no barriers to public impulses are erected and sex turns entirely into physical channels, its development ceases and the erotic life in the large sense is retarded, if not arrested. This explains the limited domestic achievements of those who, like some of the Negroes of the rural South or peasants of Europe, make courtship also an experimental mating. On the other hand, the program that permits the spreading and the deepening of the erotic craving cannot help bringing forth tension and may, because adults lack sympathy and insight, turn sex impulse toward some morbid trend. Other groups in their effort to escape tension may flee from the conflict-making dilemma of unsatisfied impulse on the one hand and conventions on the other and may turn to some substitution for their erotic craving, often work or ambition, only to find periodically that sex or love impulses break into their security and force the recognition of inner stress. This invasion, by often becoming the cause of anxiety, shame or guilt feeling, not only warps sex development but wars against the integrity of the individual.

There is also another complication which may be described best as periodicity. Certainly after puberty, more apparently in the woman than in the man, there are changes that conform to a cycle which is thoroughly individual. Sex may show great vigor as an impulse and after a few days pass to an apparent oblivion. This happens even though the changes do not take an overt sexual form. There are differences in personal emotion, differences in the individual's efficiency, differences in the pleasure-tone of the personality, even though their connection with the sex rhythm may not be recognized by the individual or by those about him.

There are two sides to sex tension, and there is need of understanding the social pressure as well as the physiological urge. It is a most fortunate child who passes safely through his contacts with adults in his early years without having shame or some degree of guilt feeling incorporated into his sex development. It is as if sex, having proved too much for adults, brings forth an uncontrollable anxiety when they first discover its appearance in their child. The reception that is accorded the faintest curiosity of the child at the moment when he distinguishes the sex equipment either of himself or of some other shows how intense and how irrational is the reaction of the average parent who is conscious of his responsibility for the sex guidance of his children. Both religious and ethical leaders are open to the same temptation and may react with such emotion or exaggeration to any expression of interest by the child as to encourage in the growing personality a morbid undercurrent regarding sex. This danger of socially perverting the normal sex impulses has grown less in recent years as parents have become better informed and more understanding. On the other hand, there have been added difficulties due to the special circumstances that beset modern parents.

We live in a time when the tempo of existence has in itself become a problem, not because it is inherently troublesome but on account of our lack of seasoning. The onrush of the modern way of living has been so sudden that we are open to its dangers, having had no time to build an immunity through contact. Every feature of our civilization reveals this. It is not, therefore, to be expected that the sex life should escape, and clearly it has not. One of the consequences is the rapid sophistication of the average boy and girl and the thrusting upon them of more mature sex knowledge and stimulation than they would have encountered at such an age in former times. We are apt to forget how rapidly we expect our young people to pass from the attitudes characteristic of the child to the social responsibilities of an adult living on the complex level of modern life. It is not strange that the more primitive impulses balk at this refinement, that there is frequently a turning back to fantasy and to standards of behavior that reveal an unsatisfied curiosity and an eager effort to understand sex.

The rapid flow of social change has swept away traditions that formerly regulated and established standards for the sex career of the unmarried. It is much like the river in the spring flood that has so changed its banks that the most experienced pilot finds none of the landmarks by which he has been in the habit of tracing his course. Sex no more than other expressions of the modern man's and woman's life escapes the difficulties of this rapid change, but what happens in this field of human experience is perhaps socially most disturbing. Sex has always been rigorously guarded by social tradition. It has been group coercion rather than individual self-discipline that has chiefly controlled sex conduct in the past, with the result that always, in a period of transition, sexual unrest, experimentation and confusion have been greatest. A considerable part of the psychic conflict of the individual reflects our social situation in this period of transition. The fact that the mores themselves are in confusion adds to the difficulties of those, who, sensitive to the social traditions and group coercions, are seeking to establish personal harmony. The task of establishing inner concord, as the primitive impulses seem to press one way and social demands the other—always difficult—is made all the greater by the prevailing social unrest and cultural disturbances of this time of rapid change.

In spite of the breaking of taboo, enough shy evasion has persisted to hamper the frank preparatory discussion of sex that young people have greatly needed in order to pass most easily through their ordeal. Feeling often only that they are out of all accord with their parents' attitudes, young men and women, meeting the full blast of machine culture, have seldom received the sympathy and understanding that they have needed to give them confidence in handling the personal problems of sex that have been forced upon them. They have been thrown into a loneliness that is unparalleled in human evolution.

In spite of this handicap, a multitude of young women and a sizable group of men, conscious of sex, have deliberately worked out a program which in most cases they have tested, often abandoned quickly, and in other cases incorporated in their later and more mature philosophy of life. Some, unwilling to reduce sex to mere physical passion, have frankly faced their body drive and, while waiting for marriage, sublimated it; others have accomplished the same task but without realizing what they were doing. In both cases the process has been essentially that of the projection of sex into other realms of conduct and interest. Sex energy is put to other uses. It acts like water turned away from the river channel and directed by the canal to the mill wheel. Sex pulsation is made a source of power to carry on lines of activity that are not at all related to the force from which they draw part of their motive and their strength.

This projection has proceeded along two different lines. One has been through the attempt to forget the turmoil of the self and to drown out the demands of sex by transference. The other projection has been through the substitution of an available relationship for that not possible, and has taken the form of fixation. The first program is commonly interpreted as a sublimation of sex. It has attracted both the man and the woman, but more often the latter. Although it takes myriad expressions, they all may be roughly classified as work, sport, or artistic creation. Many a business woman is earning more than self-support through her concentration on her daily vocation. She is also driving sex out of consciousness either fully or in part by her work. Philanthropy, science, and religion are all utilized for the same purpose and provide psychic relief in the same way. The arts provide another favored means of lessening tension. It may be either the attempt to produce for oneself in music, in painting or in literature, or it may take the less ambitious form of appreciation of the work of others. The dance also serves the same useful purpose.

Sex is also externalized and suppressed by substituting a relationship which at least has a semblance of erotic fellowship. This is the higher, the more difficult, and the more successful of the two programs. Friends, one or both parents, other people's children are the most common persons chosen for fellowship in this way of escaping strain of sex origin. If the former method carries the risk of being swept aside at any moment when sex is thoroughly aroused, this projection upon persons tends toward the danger of becoming essentially itself a sexual relation, although not admitted to be such. The fact that it is an intimate exclusive relationship permits the erotic love cravings to flow freely in a disguised form. Physiological sex is pushed into the background but psychological sex may become the very essence of the fixation. From this come tragedies. If tension is escaped for a time, it may surge again with even greater strength and with no apparent way of escape.

Throughout the sex career of the unmarried, in a great majority of cases, marriage is the goal toward which the heart is set, even when it seems far away and perhaps beyond attainment. Matrimony is nearly always the one thing most desired, at least as the finale of the first chapter of life. This thought of the ideal ultimate fulfillment has all the force of eager anticipation. By most men it is looked forward to as a certainty. In the hope of the average woman, on the contrary, there is nearly always a mixture of doubt, a recognition of the possibility of being turned aside and forced to a continuous program of sublimation. Fortunately, there is evidence of a growing freedom which permits women to express more frankly and more directly, after the manner of men, their interest in the finding and the winning of their mate. This lessens their feeling of uncertainty by offering opportunity for aggressive initiative without the necessity of putting on the former mask of subtlety.

Although no period of life is more positive and more demanding than that stretching from early puberty to

marriage, it is nearly always felt to be transitory, a prelude, negative in character as compared with the experiences of marriage. Matrimony is thought of as the socially fulfilling experience. Sex would not be nearly so great
a problem during the premarriage years if youth could
take that period seriously as a preparatory stage, providing opportunity for the gaining of self-knowledge and an
understanding of the other sex in readiness for marriage.
The tension drives imagination, and thought becomes
occupied with the idea of the ultimate outcome, marriage, with the result that the value of the period as a
preparation is at least lessened when it is not largely
lost. Failure to gain the insight required for marriage,
inability to discipline and mature sex and to establish
standards, or a precocious commitment to sex experience
that does not travel beyond its physiological origin, often
brings the man or woman to the testing of marriage
thoroughly unprepared to meet the new responsibility
and to accomplish the adjustment that successful marriage requires.

The failure to achieve a love attachment, or the necessity of a continuous postponement of marriage after one
has fallen in love, easily leads to a feeling of inferiority
that reveals itself in social attitudes entirely detached
from any apparent sex connection. The first of these has
been a problem for many young women throughout the
history of American society. The second more often dis-
turbs the young man now than was formerly the case.
The closing of the frontier, the more rigid and more
competitive organization of industry, the longer period
required for preparation for the professions and the lifting of the general standard of life, forces many men to
delay marrying, especially in the cities and in the middle
class. This inability, for economic reasons, to start mar-

riage affects both the young man and woman, but since ordinarily the first is expected to supply the necessary income, his failure to attain the position where he can do this reacts more upon him than upon the woman. One of the happy trends at present appears in the increasing willingness of young people to meet this problem by establishing an economic partnership which enables them to marry on a united income made possible by the continuance of both in gainful employment. It may be only a temporary compromise between a limited family life and none at all, but it prevents the many dangers and much of the tension of a postponed wedding.

The delay of marriage because of economic insecurity is leading to experimentation in sex relations and an attempt at a substitute for marriage. These sociological consequences of the inability to marry on account of insufficient income also have psychological meaning. There are reactions in the feeling that one is drifting away from marriage, or cannot hope to marry until many years have passed, found chiefly in the middle class among the young men and women of business or professional training. Not infrequently the attempted solution of a substitute for marriage leads all the more to the building of a chronic feeling of inferiority. The woman may come to see or to think that she is attractive only on a physical basis and that she is more removed than ever from mating on account of having accepted a liberal code of conduct. One gets the impression that the man is more likely to feel the ethical or psychic strain of behavior which collides with orthodox practices, and if he is less liable to a feeling of inferiority in comparison with the woman, he is the more open to emotional conflict, especially when he discovers that the relations he intended to keep on the level of physical comradeship have been regarded by the woman as assurance or at least as a basis for hopes of the development of an erotic fellowship that includes their marrying eventually. . . .

9.
The Kinsey Report:
Justification by Numbers

by Geoffrey Gorer

During the furor caused by the publication of *Sexual Behavior in the Human Male*, a few dissenting voices managed to be heard. Specialists particularly challenged Dr. Kinsey's "taxonomic" statistical method drawn from zoology, and his apparent neglect of certain proven psychological principles. Here, a noted British social anthropologist considers the impact of the Kinsey Report as a phenomenal best seller, and protests against the equation as "outlets" of various kinds of gonadal relief with human love. Goeffrey Gorer is the author of *The American People*, *Africa Dances*, and other studies of culture in far-flung areas of the world. Reprinted from *The American Scholar*, Summer 1948, copyright, 1948, by *The American Scholar*, by permission of the publisher.

See also Chapter 9 in *Women: "Truth and Consequences: Kinsey's Version."*

FOR THE SOCIAL SCIENTIST, a best seller is always an interesting and provocative phenomenon: what is it, he asks himself, that has made this book or play so much more acceptable to the reading public in this society at this period than the other books or plays produced at the same time? If this question can be satisfactorily answered, it invariably gives insight into the hidden wishes and fantasies of the book-reading public, and so throws light on the psychological dynamics of the society which has accepted the best seller. Even though the conscious promotion of best sellers has been very highly developed in recent years in the United States, a best seller cannot be established unless there is some congruence between its underlying material and the underlying wishes and fantasies of the purchasing public.

This year [1948] has witnessed an unparalleled phenomenon in publishing history: a dull and turgid scientific book, full of figures and tables, and published at a relatively very high price, has been selling at a rate paralleling such simple fantasies as *Gone With the Wind* or *Forever Amber.* The miscalled *Sexual Behavior in the Human Male,* by Kinsey, Pomeroy, and Martin, is firmly established in the best-seller lists. It has been the subject of numerous articles and innumerable conversations; to parallel the immediate impact of a scientific book, one would probably have to go back to 1859, and the publication of Darwin's *Origin of Species;* and even then the sales were not comparable. Of course the social penetration of this book, and indeed of any book, should not be exaggerated; even if it sells a million copies, and each copy is looked at by five people—a generous estimate—it will have reached only 3 per cent of the American population; but even this is remarkable diffusion, and calls for comment and an attempt at explanation.

The prepublication publicity campaign, with vetted articles strategically placed, was one of the most ingenious and carefully executed in recent publishing history; and undoubtedly a certain number of purchasers bought the book in the hope of pornographic titillation. But if this had been its main drawing power, its sales would have quickly dropped, for few texts dealing with such a subject could be less stimulating. Nor, in such a case, would it have received the long and solemn digests, in lieu of reviews or criticisms, which appeared in most of the public press.

I do not intend here to criticize the book from a scientific point of view. Competent specialists have pointed out, or will point out, the unsatisfactory nature of the sample on which Dr. Kinsey bases his generalizations; the dubious practice of treating memories of sexual behavior many years ago as absolutely veridic, when no law court will accept unsupported testimony of any event in the distant past; the ignoring of the accumulated psychiatric knowledge of the last fifty years on sexual behavior, and the (surely willful) distortion of the theories and viewpoints of psychiatry. If this book had only been bought by specialists competent to criticize it, its impact as a social phenomenon would have been minute; but the vast mass of the readers, like the reviewers, accept the material uncritically, so that it is true for them. On this basis, what can one deduce about the attitudes and expectations of college-educated urban Americans (far and away the largest component in Dr. Kinsey's sample, and almost certainly also in his customers) from the contents of the book, its reception in the popular press, and its echoes in conversation?

The chief novelty in the material, and the aspect which has been most consistently stressed, is the demonstration that certain types of sexual behavior are more widely practiced than had hitherto been supposed. That is all. No moderately sophisticated person can have been unaware that such practices existed; Dr. Kinsey has provided figures of distribution.

Why then has such a pother been made about these figures of distribution? Why have reviewers stated, in various synonyms, that the book contains "potential dynamite"? Why have there been numerous suggestions that, in the light of these "disclosures," the laws meant to regulate sexual behavior and the instructions and admonitions given to young people will all have to be changed?

I suggest that this springs from what is in some ways the fundamental democratic fallacy, which may be called Justification by Numbers. If a few people do or think something, it may be wrong; but if a lot of people do or think it, then it is obviously right. This argument underlies a great deal of American advertising: to state that the brand you are marketing is the "most popular brand" or "sells more than double its nearest competitor" is to suggest forcibly that it is therefore better. On the political level the votes of the majority should undoubtedly be decisive on those issues on which they are called upon to vote (and these are remarkably few); but to extend this principle to moral, psychological or physiological activities is completely illogical.

An illustration may make this clearer. A colleague of Dr. Kinsey conducts a survey in Germany entitled *Eating Behavior in the Human Male* and finds that, say, 80 per cent of the sample has a calory "intake" of 1500 units daily, that 73 per cent only have two dietetic "intakes" daily, and so on and so forth; in the light of his "disclosures" it will become clear that 1500 calories daily divided into two meals is "normal" eating behavior, and that all our views on dietetics and nourishment have to be revised.

Most people would reject this as obvious nonsense, for we have scientifically determined standards of adequate nourishment, which have nothing to do with temporary and local practices; but the arguments are as valid in the one case as the other. The scientific determination of adequate and satisfying sexual behavior is by no means so well established or agreed upon (for, despite Dr. Kinsey, the implications of sex are much more complicated), but they will not be determined by a study of distribution. Dr. Kinsey's figures *can* be interpreted to mean that neurotic disturbances in sexual life in the contemporary United States are as widespread as malnutrition in contemporary Germany.

I do not mean to suggest by this that it would not be highly desirable to change or modify the laws of the various states which are meant to control sexual behavior; but an unjust law does not change in injustice if it potentially affects 30 per cent of the population instead of 3 per cent. At most it makes the savage punishment of those who are convicted even more arbitrary than it had appeared before.

A second important aspect of this book is what might be called the "atomization" of sex. Until Dr. Kinsey came along, sex had generally been viewed as one of the most complex of all human activities, involving not merely the genital organs, but all the psychological and emotional components of the personality, both conscious and unconscious. But with Dr. Kinsey, everything except overt genital behavior has been omitted; sex has been reduced to statistics.

This atomization is in congruence with one of the major trends in contemporary American culture. The triumphs of mass production have been produced by the calculated atomization of the manufacturing process and of the worker's movements. The atomization of knowledge into a series of discrete and equal facts can be seen from the intelligence tests administered to preschool moppets to the check lists which in many colleges constitute the chief examination before proceeding to graduate studies; from the "quiz" shows to the crossword puzzle; from teaching temporary officers new techniques, to public opinion polls. Now sex has been added to the list.

By thus oversimplifying or atomizing sex, it is possible to indulge in this domain too in the popular and widespread American habit of rating oneself. One of the chief recurring motives throughout American life from infancy to old age is the striving for relative success with one's equals and near equals: precocity, marks or grades at school, athletic success, relative income, popularity—the list could be indefinitely prolonged. This "self-rating" has become so emotionally important for so many Americans that the greater number of popular papers have scoring cards by which one can rate oneself for knowledge or for the possession of certain qualities (20 to 16, excellent; 15 to 11, good; 10 to 6, average; under 6, poor). Now Dr. Kinsey has supplied a great number of tables by which one can rate oneself; and, in an appendix, has thoughtfully broken them down by age, education, marital status, etc. With a little trouble one can find out how one stacks up in frequency of "outlet," variety of "outlet," and even more intimate anatomical details, with one's peers. "Keeping up with the Joneses" acquires a new, and perhaps slightly ribald, significance.

As in all such "self-rating" tables, admiration goes to the high scores. Behind the mask of dispassionateness, one can easily discern Dr. Kinsey's astonished admiration for the people with the larger rates of "outlet," and his contemptuous pity for those making poor scores. A little anthropological knowledge might have rectified this attitude. We have enough information from enough primitive societies to suggest that there is an (apparently) direct correlation between high rates of intercourse and lack of emotional interest in sex or belief in love; the Lepchas from the borders of Tibet, whom I studied, had rates of outlet in their early adult life which would make Dr. Kinsey's high scorers look like pikers. For the

Lepchas, sex was a satisfaction no more important than food; they did not believe in love, made no allowances for it, and the exclusive possession of a spouse was legally impossible. As a matter of fact, Dr. Kinsey probably already had the evidence to confirm this; among his highest scorers are his ubiquitous male prostitutes (p. 216) —a group which surely figures rather more importantly in Dr. Kinsey's sample than in the population at large. To equal the performances of such people is perhaps not wholly enviable.

It may be remarked that these "self-rating" tables are liable to produce more disquietude than satisfaction in the people who consult them. Forty-nine per cent of the population is always below the median. People so unsure of themselves as to need support from "self-rating" are not too likely to get it. On the other hand, judging by previous experience, people who are disturbed about their "deviance" will not get psychological comfort for more than a very few days from the tabular demonstration that their deviations are more widespread than they had suspected.

A probable by-product of these rating scales may well be further ammunition for the anti-intellectualism which is already widespread. In comic books and cartoons, professors are always "long-haired," and scientists are always "mad"; now Dr. Kinsey brings evidence to show that, compared with the less educated, they are less "manly," "make" fewer girls, and sleep less often with their wives than do the men who leave school as soon as it is legally possible. The implications are obvious.

To parody a phrase of Marxist dialectics, Dr. Kinsey's tables result in the devaluation of all values. An involuntary nocturnal emission, a little boy sliding down a rope, a murderous rape, or Romeo spending the night with

Juliet, Damon with Pythias, Paolo with Francesca, are all equated as one "outlet"; physiological itch, lust and love are reduced to their lowest common denominator, and it couldn't well be lower. Just as the dollar which may save oneself or one's family from starvation is no different from the dollar added to the billionaire's bank deposit, so in Dr. Kinsey's treatment all sexual "outlets" are reduced to a dead level of physiological spasm. Like dollars, the more you have the better. Chastity, even though it be Abélard's, results in a low score; and who wants to rate low?

Inspection of the tables suggests a couple of further generalizations about the men whom Dr. Kinsey interviewed. They do not easily tolerate physiological discomfort, and will get rid of it some way or other. Just as there is in the United States very low tolerance of even mild hunger or thirst or cold—as witnessed by the corner drugstore, the numerous drinking fountains, the central heating—so relatively mild gonadal pressure will be relieved somehow, almost as a health measure.

Secondly, despite the devaluation of all values, people are seeking for a greater level of satisfaction in sex than can generally be achieved. This I think is the explanation for much of the premarital, extramarital and occasional homosexual behavior which Dr. Kinsey demonstrates. Some of these excursions may be due to the search for a "good time" under the influence of alcohol, some to adolescent experimentation; but much would seem to be due to the seeking for an unattainable ideal.

I should be unhappy if it were deduced from this article that I am opposed to the scientific investigation of sexual behavior; on the contrary, I think it is one of the most important gaps in our knowledge of contemporary society which, when filled, may do much to remedy the disquietudes and restlessness of this Age of Anxiety. But it needs a more integrated approach than that of an entomologist; an act which can consummate love and produce children cannot be measured with the calipers that determine the variation in the wingspan of wasps. For a society which believes in love, be it sacred or profane, the physiological aspect of sex cannot be separated from its emotional and psychological concomitants without reducing it to meaninglessness. We need statistical studies of human sexual behavior, but they should be studies of the behavior of human beings, not of genital organs.

To revert to the original query of why the Kinsey report has had so widespread and ready an acceptance in the United States today, I think the answer can be found on two levels. It does not contain a single novel or disturbing idea, no new insight into human behavior, such as caused the initial rejection of such pioneers as Havelock Ellis or Sigmund Freud; and its underlying attitudes are in complete congruence with some of the predominant, though not necessarily the most valuable, attitudes and ideas of contemporary, educated, urban Americans. To the extent that Justification by Numbers is a valid concept, the phenomenal sales of Dr. Kinsey's book demonstrate that he has provided what his public wanted.

10.
Homosexual Love

by Edward Westermarck

Hypotheses on the primary causes of homosexuality are offered in several of the selections in this volume, notably those of Freud, Havelock Ellis, and Dr. Menninger. In the companion volume, Women, Dr. Clara Thompson surveys current psycho-analytic concepts of the problem. But the deviant manifestation of the sexual impulse has been known at all stages of cultural and historical development by every race of mankind in every part of the world. This background information is reviewed here with the scope typical of the erudition of this famous historian of marriage and morals. Reprinted from The Origin and Development of the Moral Ideas by Edward Westermarck, Macmillan and Company Ltd., 1912, by permission of the Estate of Edward Westermarck.

See also Chapters 2, 8, 10, 11 in Women: "Prepuberty in Woman," "The Unmarried," "Changing Concepts of Homosexuality," "The Abnormality of Prostitution."

OUR REVIEW OF THE MORAL IDEAS concerning sexual relations has not yet come to an end. The gratification of the sexual instinct assumes forms which fall outside the ordinary pale of nature. Of these there is one which, on account of the role it has played in the moral history of mankind, cannot be passed over in silence, namely, intercourse between individuals of the same sex, what is nowadays commonly called homosexual love.

It is frequently met with among the lower animals. It probably occurs, at least sporadically, among every race of mankind. And among some peoples it has assumed such proportions as to form a true national habit.

In America homosexual customs have been observed

among a great number of native tribes. In nearly every part of the continent there seem to have been, since ancient times, men dressing themselves in the clothes and performing the functions of women, and living with other men as their concubines or wives. Moreover, between young men who are comrades in arms there are *liaisons d'amitié,* which, according to Lafitau, "contain much vice though they permit no sign of it to show."*

Homosexual practices are, or have been, very prominent among the peoples in the neighborhood of Behring Sea. In Kadiak it was the custom of the parent who had a girl-like son to try to dress and rear him as a girl, teaching him only domestic duties, keeping him at woman's work, and letting him associate only with women and girls. Arriving at the age of ten or fifteen years, he was married to some wealthy man and was then called an *achnuchik* or *shoopan.* Dr. Borgoras gives the following account of a similar practice prevalent among the Chukchi: "It happens frequently that, under the supernatural influence of one of their shamans, or priests, a Chukchi lad at sixteen years of age will suddenly relinquish his sex and imagine himself to be a woman. He adopts a woman's attire, lets his hair grow, and devotes himself altogether to female occupation. Furthermore, this disowner of his sex takes a husband into the *Yurt* and does all the work which is usually incumbent on the wife in most unnatural and voluntary subjection. Thus it frequently happens in a *Yurt* that the husband is a woman, while the wife is a man! . . ."

The change of sex was usually accompanied by future shamanship; indeed, nearly all the shamans were former

*Prof. Westermarck's extensive documentation of his source material, which runs to many pages in the original, has been eliminated here.—Ed.

delinquents of their sex. Among the Chukchi male
shamans who are clothed in woman's attire and are believed to be transformed physically into women are still
quite common; and traces of the change of the shaman's
sex into that of a woman may be found among many
other Siberian tribes. In some cases at least there can be
no doubt that these transformations were connected with
homosexual practices. In his description of the Koriaks,
Krasheninnikoff makes mention of the *ké yev,* that is,
men occupying the position of concubines; and he compares them with the Kamchadale *koé kcuc,* as he calls
them, that is, men transformed into women. Every *koé
kcuc,* he says, is regarded as a magician and interpreter
of dreams; but from his confused description Mr. Jochel-
son thinks it may be inferred that the most important
feature of the institution of the *koé kcuc,* lay, not in
their shamanistic power, but in their position with regard to the satisfaction of the unnatural inclinations of
the Kamchadales. The *koé kcuc* wore women's clothes,
did women's work, and were in the position of wives or
concubines.

. . . Homosexual love is reported as common among
the Marshall Islanders and in Hawaii. From Tahiti we
hear of a set of men called by the natives *mahoos,* who
assume the dress, attitude, and manners, of women, and
affect all the fantastic oddities and coquetries of the
vainest of females. They mostly associate with the wom-
en, who court their acquaintance. With the manners of
women, they adopt their peculiar employments. . . . The
encouragement of this abomination is almost solely confined to the chiefs. . . .

Among the natives of the Kimberley District in West
Australia, if a young man on reaching a marriageable
age can find no wife, he is presented with a boy-wife,

known as *chookadoo*. In this case, also, the ordinary exogamic rules are observed, and the "husband" has to avoid his "mother-in-law" just as if he were married to a woman. The *chookadoo* is a boy of five years to about ten, when he is initiated. "The relations which exist between him and his protecting *billalu*," says Mr. Hardman, "are somewhat doubtful. There is no doubt they have connection, but the natives repudiate with horror and disgust the idea of sodomy." Such marriages are evidently exceedingly common. As the women are generally monopolized by the older and more influential men of the tribe, it is rare to find a man under thirty or forty who has a wife; hence it is the rule that, when a boy becomes five years old, he is given as a boy-wife to one of the young men. According to Mr. Purcell's description of the natives of the same district, "every useless member of the tribe" gets a boy, about five or seven years old; and these boys, who are called *mullawongahs*, are used for sexual purposes. Among the Chingalee of South Australia, Northern Territory, old men are often noticed with no wives but accompanied by one or two boys, whom they jealously guard and with whom they have sodomitic intercourse. . . .

In Madagascar there are certain boys who live like women and have intercourse with men, paying those men who please them. . . .

In China, where it is also extremely common, there are special houses devoted to male prostitution, and boys are sold by their parents about the age of four, to be trained for this occupation. In Japan pederasty is said by some to have prevailed from the most ancient times, whereas others are of the opinion that it was introduced by Buddhism about the sixth century of our era. The monks used to live with handsome youths, to whom they were often passionately devoted; and in feudal times nearly every knight had as his favorite a young man with whom he entertained relations of the most intimate kind, and on behalf of whom he was always ready to fight a duel when the occasion occurred. Teahouses with male *geishas* were found in Japan till the middle of the nineteenth century. Nowadays pederasty seems to be more prevalent in the Southern than in the Northern provinces of the country, but there are also districts where it is hardly known.

No reference is made to pederasty either in the Homeric poems or by Hesiod, but later on we meet with it almost as a national institution in Greece. It was known in Rome and other parts of Italy at an early period; but here also it became much more frequent in the course of time. At the close of the sixth century, Polybius tells us, many Romans paid a *talent* for the possession of a beautiful youth. During the Empire "it was the custom among patrician families to present to the boy at home a male slave of the same age as a sleeping companion with whom he could satisfy his first sexual urges"; and formal marriages between men were introduced with all the solemnities of ordinary nuptials. . . .

The above statements chiefly refer to homosexual practices between men, but similar practices also occur between women. Among the American aborigines there are not only men who behave like women, but women who behave like men. Thus in certain Brazilian tribes women are found who abstain from every womanly occupation and imitate the men in everything, who wear their hair in masculine fashion, who go to war with a bow and arrows, who hunt together with the men, and who would rather allow themselves to be killed than have sexual intercourse with a man. "Each of these women has a woman who serves her and with whom she says she is married; they live together as husband and wife." So also there are among the Eastern Eskimo some women who refuse to accept husbands, preferring to adopt masculine manners, following the deer on the mountains, trapping and fishing for themselves. Homosexual practices are said to be common among Hottentot and Herero women. In Zanzibar there are women who wear men's clothes in private, show a preference for masculine occupations, and seek sexual satisfaction among women who have the same inclination, or else among normal women who are won over by presents or other means. In Egyptian harems every woman is said to have a "friend." In Bali homosexuality is almost as common among women as among men, though it is exercised more secretly; and the same seems to be the case in India. From Greek antiquity we hear of "Lesbian" love. The fact that homosexuality has been much more frequently noticed in men than in women does not imply that the latter are less addicted to it. For various reasons the sexual abnormalities of women have attracted much less attention, and moral opinion has generally taken little notice of them.

. . . A very important cause of homosexual practices is absence of the other sex. There are many instances of this among the lower animals. Buffon long ago observed that, if male or female birds of various species were shut up together, they would soon begin to have sexual relations among themselves, the males sooner than the females. The West Australian boy-marriage is a substitute for ordinary marriage in cases when women are not obtainable. Among the Bororo of Brazil homosexual intercourse is said to occur in their men-houses only when the scarcity of accessible girls is unusually great. Its prev-

alence in Tahiti may perhaps be connected with the fact
that there was only one woman to four or five men,
owing to the habit of female infanticide. Among the
Chinese in certain regions, for instance Java, the lack of
accessible women is the principal cause of homosexual
practices. According to some writers such practices are
the results of polygamy. In Mohammedan countries they
are no doubt largely due to the seclusion of women, pre-
venting free intercourse between the sexes and compelling the unmarried people to associate almost exclusively with members of their own sex. Among the moun-
taineers of northern Morocco the excessive indulgence
in pederasty thus goes hand in hand with great isolation
of the women and a very high standard of female chastity, whereas among the Arabs of the plains, who are
little addicted to boy-love, the unmarried girls enjoy considerable freedom. Both in Asia and Europe the obliga-
tory celibacy of the monks and priests has been a cause
of homosexual practices, though it must not be forgotten
that a profession which imposes abstinence from marriage is likely to attract a comparatively large number of
congenital inverts. The temporary separation of the sexes
involved in a military mode of life no doubt accounts
for the extreme prevalence of homosexual love among
warlike races, like the Sikhs, Afghans, Dorains, and Nor-
mans. In Persia and Morocco it is particularly common
among soldiers. In Japan it was an incident of knight-
hood, in New Caledonia and North America of brother-
hood in arms. . . .

I take the case to be, that homosexual practices in
early youth have had a lasting effect on the sexual instinct, which at its first appearance, being somewhat in-
definite, is easily turned into a homosexual direction. In
Morocco inversion is most prevalent among the scribes,

who from childhood have lived in very close association with their fellow students. Of course, influences of this kind "require a favorable organic predisposition to act on"; but this predisposition is probably no abnormality at all, only a feature in the ordinary sexual constitution of man. It should be noticed that the most common form of inversion, at least in Mohammedan countries, is love of boys or youths not yet in the age of puberty, that is, of male individuals who are physically very like girls. Voltaire observes: "Often a boy will, by the freshness of his skin, the glow of his complexion and the softness of his eyes resemble a beautiful girl for two or three years; if he is loved it is nature's doing." Moreover, in normal cases sexual attraction depends not only on sex, but on a youthful appearance as well; and there are persons so constituted that to them the latter factor is of chief importance, whilst the question of sex is almost a matter of indifference.

In ancient Greece, also, not only homosexual intercourse, but actual inversion, seems to have been very common; and although this, like every form of love, must have contained a congenital element, there can be little doubt, I think, that it was largely due to external circumstances of a social character. It may, in the first place, be traced to the methods of training the youth. In Sparta it seems to have been the practice for every youth of good character to have his lover, or "inspirator," and for every well-educated man to be the lover of some youth. The relations between the "inspirator" and the "listener" were extremely intimate: at home the youth was constantly under the eyes of his lover, who was supposed to be to him a model and pattern of life; in battle they stood near one another and their fidelity and affection were often shown till death; if his relatives were absent, the youth might be represented in the public assembly by his lover; and for many faults, particularly want of ambition, the lover could be punished instead of the "listener." This ancient custom prevailed with still greater force in Crete, which island was hence by many persons considered to be the place of its birth. Whatever may have been the case originally, there can be no doubt that in later times the relations between the youth and his lover implied unchaste intercourse. And in other Greek states the education of the youth was accompanied by similar consequences. At an early age the boy was taken away from his mother, and spent thenceforth all his time in the company of men, until he reached the age when marriage became for him a civic duty. According to Plato, the gymnasia and common meals among the youth "seem always to have had a tendency to degrade the ancient and natural custom of love below the level, not only of man, but of the beasts." Plato also mentions the effect which these habits had on the sexual instincts of the men: "When they reached manhood they were lovers of youths and not naturally inclined to marry or beget children, but if at all, they did so only in obedience to the law." Is not this, in all probability, an instance of acquired inversion? But besides the influence of education there was another factor which, co-operating with it, favored the development of homosexual tendencies, namely, the great gulf which mentally separated the sexes. Nowhere else has the difference in culture between men and women been so immense as in the fully developed Greek civilization. The lot of a wife in Greece was retirement and ignorance. She lived in almost absolute seclusion, in a separate part of the house, together with her female slaves, deprived of all the educating influence of male society, and having no place at those public spectacles which were the chief means of culture. In such circumstances it is not difficult to understand that men so highly intellectual as those of Athens regarded the love of women as the offspring of the common Aphrodite, who "is the body rather than the soul." They had reached a stage of mental culture at which the sexual instinct normally has a craving for refinement, at which the gratification of mere physical lust appears brutal. In the eyes of the most refined among them those who were inspired by the heavenly Aphrodite loved neither women nor boys, but intelligent beings whose reason was beginning to be developed, much about the time at which the beards began to grow. . . . So also it seems that the ignorance and dullness of Mohammedan women, which is a result of their total lack of education and their secluded life, is a cause of homosexual practices; Moors are sometimes heard to defend pederasty on the plea that the company of boys, who always have news to tell, is so much more entertaining than the company of women.

We have hitherto dealt with homosexual love as a fact; we shall now pass to the moral valuation to which it is subject. Where it occurs as a national habit we may assume that no censure, or no severe censure, is passed on it. Among the Bataks of Sumatra there is no punishment for it. . . . There is no indication that the North American aborigines attached any opprobrium to men who had intercourse with those members of their own sex who had assumed the dress and the habits of women. In Kadiak such a companion was on the contrary regarded as a great acquisition; and the effeminate men, far from being despised, were held in repute by the people, most of them being wizards. We have previously noticed the connection between homosexual practices and shaman-

ism among the various Siberian peoples; and it is said
that such shamans as had changed their sex were greatly
feared by the people, being regarded as very powerful.
. . . The Incas themselves were not only free from such
practices in their own persons, they would not even
permit any one who was guilty of them to remain in the
royal houses or palaces. . . . In several of the more remote provinces of Mexico sodomy was tolerated, if not
actually permitted, because the people believed that their
gods were addicted to it; and it is not improbable that
in earlier times the same was the case in the entire empire. But in a later age severe measures were adopted by
legislators in order to suppress the practice. In Mexico
people found guilty of it were killed. In Nicaragua it
was punished capitally by stoning, and none of the Maya
nations was without strict laws against it. . . .

Homosexual practices are said to be taken little notice
of even by some uncivilized peoples who are not addicted
to them. . . . The East African Masai do not punish
sodomy. But we also meet with statements of a contrary
nature. In a Kafir tribe Mr. Warner heard of a case of
it—the only one during a residence of twenty-five years—
which was punished with a fine of some cattle claimed
by the chief. Among the Ondonga pederasts are hated,
and the men who behave like women are detested, most
of them being wizards. . . .

In Morocco active pederasty is regarded with almost
complete indifference, whilst the passive sodomite, if a
grown-up individual, is spoken of with scorn. . . . Among
the Hindus it is said to be held in abhorrence, but their
sacred books deal with it leniently. According to the
Laws of Manu, "a twice-born man who commits an unnatural offense with a male, or has intercourse with a
female in a cart drawn by oxen, in water, or in the day-

time shall bathe, dressed in his clothes"; and all these are reckoned as minor offenses.

Chinese law makes little distinction between unnatural and other sexual offenses. An unnatural offense is variously considered according to the age of the patient, and whether or not consent was given. . . . In Japan there was no law against homosexual intercourse till the revolution of 1868. In the period of Japanese chivalry it was considered more heroic if a man loved a person of his own sex than if he loved a woman; and nowadays people are heard to say that in those provinces of the country where pederasty is widely spread the men are more manly and robust than in those where it does not prevail.

The laws of the ancient Scandinavians ignore homosexual practices; but passive pederasts were much despised by them. They were identified with cowards and regarded as sorcerers. . . . It is certain that the opprobrium which the pagan Scandinavians attached to homosexual love was chiefly restricted to him who played the woman's part. In one of the poems the hero even boasts of being the father of offspring borne by another man.

In Sparta it was necessary that the "listener" should accept the "inspirator" from real affection; he who did so out of pecuniary consideration was punished by the ephors. . . . But the universal rule in Greece seems to have been that when decorum was observed in the friendship between a man and a youth, no inquiries were made into the details of the relationship. And this attachment was not only regarded as permissible, but was praised as the highest and purest form of love, as the offspring of the heavenly Aphrodite, as a path leading to virtue, as a weapon against tyranny, as a safeguard of civic liberty, as a source of national greatness and glory. Phaedrus said he knew no greater blessing to a young man who is be-

ginning life than a virtuous lover, or to the lover than
a beloved youth; for the principle which ought to be the
guide of men who would lead a noble life cannot be
implanted by any other motive so well as by love. The
Platonic Pausanias argued that if love of youths is held
in ill repute it is so only because it is inimical to tyranny;
"the interests of rulers require that their subjects should
be poor in spirit, and that there should be no strong
bond of friendship or society among them, which love,
above all other motives, is likely to inspire." . . .

In the Zoroastrian books "unnatural sin" is treated
with a severity to which there is a parallel only in He-
brewism and Christianity. According to the Vendidad,
there is no atonement for it. It is punished with torments
in the other world, and is capital here below. Even he
who committed it involuntarily, by force, is subject to
corporal punishment. Indeed, it is a more heinous sin
than the slaying of a righteous man. "There is no worse
sin than this in the good religion, and it is proper to
call those who commit it worthy of death in reality. If
any one comes forth to them, and shall see them in the
act, and is working with an axe, it is requisite for him
to cut off the heads or to rip up the bellies of both, and
it is no sin for him. But it is not proper to kill any person
without the authority of high priests and kings, except
on account of committing or permitting unnatural intercourse."

Nor are unnatural sins allowed to defile the land of
the Lord. Whosoever shall commit such abominations,
be he Israelite or stranger dwelling among the Israelites,
shall be put to death, the souls that do them shall be cut
off from their people. By unnatural sins of lust the
Canaanites polluted their land, so that God visited their
guilt, and the land spewed out its inhabitants.

This horror of homosexual practices was shared by Christianity. According to St. Paul, they form the climax of the moral corruption to which God gave over the heathen because of their apostasy from him. Tertullian says that they are banished "not only from the threshold, but from all shelter of the church, because they are no sins, but monstrosities." St. Basil maintains that they deserve the same punishment as murder, idolatry, and witchcraft. According to a decree of the Council of Elvira, those who abuse boys to satisfy their lusts are denied communion even at their last hour. In no other point of morals was the contrast between the teachings of Christianity and the habits and opinions of the world over which it spread more radical than in this. In Rome there was an old law of unknown date, called Lex Scantinia (or Scatinia), which imposed a mulct on him who committed pederasty with a free person; but this law, of which very little is known, had lain dormant for ages, and the subject of ordinary homosexual intercourse had never afterwards attracted the attention of the pagan legislators. But when Christianity became the religion of the Roman Empire, a veritable crusade was opened against it. Constantius and Constans made it a capital crime, punishable with the sword. Valentinian went further still and ordered that those who were found guilty of it should be burned alive in the presence of all the people. Justinian, terrified by certain famines, earthquakes, and pestilences, issued an edict which again condemned persons guilty of unnatural offenses to the sword, "lest, as the result of these impious acts, whole cities should perish together with their inhabitants," as we are taught by Holy Scripture that through such acts cities have perished with the men in them. "A sentence of

death and infamy," says Gibbon, "was often founded on
the slight and suspicious evidence of a child or a servant
. . . and pederasty became the crime of those to whom
no crime could be imputed."

This attitude toward homosexual practices had a profound and lasting influence on European legislation.
Throughout the Middle Ages and later, Christian law-
givers thought that nothing but a painful death in the
flames could atone for the sinful act. In England Fleta
speaks of the offender being buried alive; but we are
elsewhere told that burning was the due punishment. . . .
In France persons were actually burned for this crime in
the middle and latter part of the eighteenth century. But
in this, as in so many other respects, the rationalistic
movement of that age brought about a change. To punish sodomy with death, it was said, is atrocious; when
unconnected with violence, the law ought to take no
notice of it at all. It does not violate any other person's
right, its influence on society is merely indirect, like that
of drunkenness and free love; it is a disgusting vice, but
its only proper punishment is contempt. This view was
adopted by the French "Code penal," according to which
homosexual practices in private, between two consenting
adult parties, whether men or women, are absolutely un-
punished. The homosexual act is treated as a crime only
when it implies an outrage on public decency, or when
there is violence or absence of consent, or when one of
the parties is under age or unable to give valid consent.
This method of dealing with homosexuality has been
followed by the legislators of various European countries, and in those where the law still treats the act in
question per se as a penal offense, notably in Germany,
a propaganda in favor of its alteration is carried on with

the support of many men of scientific eminence. This changed attitude of the law toward homosexual intercourse undoubtedly indicates a change of moral opinions. Though it is impossible to measure exactly the degree of moral condemnation, I suppose that few persons nowadays attach to it the same enormity of guilt as did our forefathers. And the question has even been put whether morality has anything at all to do with a sexual act, committed by the mutual consent of two adult individuals, which is productive of no offspring, and which on the whole concerns the welfare of nobody but the parties themselves. . . .

So also the Hebrews' abhorrence of sodomy was largely due to their hatred of a foreign cult. . . .

The Hebrew conception of homosexual love to some extent affected Mohammedanism, and passed into Christianity. The notion that it is a form of sacrilege was here strengthened by the habits of the gentiles. St. Paul found the abominations of Sodom prevalent among nations who had "changed the truth of God into a lie, and worshipped and served the creature more than the Creator." During the Middle Ages heretics were accused of unnatural vice as a matter of course. Indeed, so closely was sodomy associated with heresy that the same name was applied to both. . . . In medieval laws sodomy was also repeatedly mentioned together with heresy, and the punishment was the same for both. . . . Very naturally, therefore, it has come to be regarded with somewhat great leniency by law and public opinion in proportion as they have emancipated themselves from theological doctrines. And the fresh light which the scientific study of the sexual impulse has lately thrown upon the subject of homosexuality must also necessarily influence the moral ideas relating to it, in so far as no scrutinizing judge can fail to take into account the pressure which a powerful nonvolitional desire exercises upon an agent's will.

11.
The Prostitute and Her Customers

by Oswald Schwarz, M.D.

A humanistic definition of prostitution as "sexual gratification separated from personal union" enables Dr. Schwarz to evaluate this form of sex activity as a distorted human relationship rather than a moral or economic problem. An outstanding Viennese urological surgeon, Oswald Schwarz later studied medical psychology, and concentrated on the treatment of sexual disorders. He is the author of *Diagnosis and Treatment of Organic Symptoms of Mental Origin* and several books on sex pathology. Reprinted from *The Psychology of Sex* by Oswald Schwarz, M.D., Pelican Book, 1949, by permission of Penguin Books Ltd.

See also Chapter 11 in Women: "The Abnormality of Prostitution."

THE EXISTENCE OF PROSTITUTION is neither an essentially moral nor a purely social-economic problem; in fact it comprises both these elements of our existence, and some others. It is a fact much too little known, or at any rate recognized, that prostitution has existed ever since, and everywhere that, men have lived in a community. The fame of the Greek hetaerae and of the Japanese geishas, and the fact that barren women in South Sea islands are expelled into the woods at the service of any man, testify to the antiquity and ubiquity of this institution.

Prostitution belongs essentially to civilization, as the shadow belongs to the light, and only because the shadow deepens as the light brightens is prostitution—or so at least it seems—much more widely spread nowadays than it was in the past. In a previous chapter I have described one aspect of the mentality of civilized man as the capacity to postpone the immediate satisfaction of a physical urge. During the growth of civilization this virtue has been turned into the fateful technique separating the component elements of life's complex wholeness; form from content, values from facts, pleasure from need, soul from body, profit from labor, business from morals. *Prostitution begins when sexual gratification is separated from personal union.* These few examples, which could easily be added to, show that prostitution is nothing more or less than the manifestation in the sexual field of the basic dualism of the civilized mentality. An additional reason why prostitution is found less frequently in primitive societies than in higher ones probably lies in the fact that economic difficulties grow with the degree of civilization and prevent young people from marrying when they become sexually mature. Thus the attempt to fight this social evil by legal means on the sexual front alone must prove as certain a failure as did the experiment of prohibition in the United States, or the attempt to stop dope traffic by customs regulation, or to end wars by old-fashioned diplomatic antics.

Nothing short of a spiritual revolution would be sufficient to rectify the sexual as well as some other effects of our way of living. A purely economic revolution would not do, as the experience of Russia proved in the early years of the Soviets. The new regime tried to combat prostitution as one of the evils typical of capitalistic economy, and succeeded beyond belief—but for a very unexpected reason: an important item in the program of the social reorganization was the abolition of the institution of marriage as part of the complete atomization of society; this resulted at once in a hitherto unheard-of lowering of sexual morality to the level of extreme promiscuity. Consequently professional prostitution became unnecessary, because the whole of Russia turned—as Lenin himself described it to Clara Zetkin—into a gigantic brothel.*

According to common opinion, a prostitute is a woman who accepts monetary reward for an essentially unsaleable commodity. And if one does not limit this bargain to the taking just of money, but applies the term, as one is perfectly justified in doing from a psychological point of view, to any woman who puts a price on something essentially priceless, the full magnitude of the problem clearly emerges. For it is not only the girl who sells her poor attraction on a dark street corner who prostitutes herself, but also the American millionairess who marries the European heir to an aristocratic title, and all the legion of women in between these extremes who use their favors as something to bargain with.

It is interesting to recall that the acceptance of a reward in money or kind was not always considered the characteristic of prostitution. According to ancient Roman law, for instance, a prostitute was a woman who offered herself *passim et sine delectu* (everywhere and without pleasure). Observe how much more human than ours this concept is, because it stresses just that lack of emotional participation which lowers the sexual act to a mere genital function and thus constitutes the essential, as distinct from the conventional, immorality of prostitution. Incidentally, the men who frequent prostitutes make themselves guilty of the same offense, because those who pay a price are equal partners with those who accept it. That this has not yet been sufficiently acknowledged,

*By the mid thirties, passage of a law which forbade abortions, increasing campaigns against sexual irresponsibility, and a tightening of divorce procedures had begun to stabilize sex relations within the framework of marriage.—Ed.

and the odium of prostitution, reserved for the woman only, is probably due to the fact that moral codes have always been made by men.

Now, what sort of women volunteer for the sorry trade of prostitution? Careful investigations have proved that the genuine prostitute is not only morally, but also mentally, defective. She lacks a sense of the cardinal value, the value of the human person, and consequently of all values derived from it, including the value of community and work. She is lazy, vain, irresponsible, prodigal, unsettled, etc. But one thing she never is: oversexed. And it is part of her general infantilism that she uses the genital function as a means of obtaining non-sexual aims, just as children do. The existence of the "timeless prostitute type," as Lombroso termed it, has often been confirmed. The German psychiatrist Schneider, assisted by a surprisingly large number of kind people, made the experiment of placing a sufficient number of these girls in private houses as domestics, companions, and the like. After one year 85 per cent had run away, preferring their sordid previous existence to any sort of social comfort which had to be paid for by work. Besides these genuine prostitutes, who never had a personality, we find another very large group of women who throw their personality away at the bidding of a neurotic impulse. And the most essential and precious part of a woman's personality, her femininity, goes overboard first. Her sense of inferiority devalues this most valuable and vulnerable part of herself, and makes such a woman throw away her body in despair, or use it as a means of self-justification, or offer it gratuitously to any man who asks for it. Some of these women do it in a kind of missionary spirit, looking at their beauty as common property, which everybody has a right to enjoy—and there are sometimes lovely characters among these unfortunates. From this disposition it is only a small step to the so-called "temple prostitution" as practiced in ancient Babylon, Armenia, Greece, and India. It is a strange paradox that what from a psychological point of view must be condemned as essentially immoral could be put to the service of religious ceremony. Priestesses offer themselves to the priests or worshippers as part of the holy service. Another strange example of how closely the highest in human existence is linked with the lowest. In this context must also be mentioned the *jus primae noctis,* or the *droit du seigneur,* a custom which gave the king or feudal lord the right to spend with the young bride the first night after her marriage to one of his subjects. Relevant also is the custom among exotic peoples for a host to offer his wife or daughters to the guest, or for friends to interchange their wives temporarily, as proof of their devotion to each other. These customs have been observed in places as remote and far away from each other as ancient Peru, North America, and Polynesia. They have been practiced among Eskimos and in medieval Europe. Various explanations have been propounded for them, but I think the true one lies in the same mental immaturity as causes masturbation in young children: nonsexual emotions (sense of power, hospitality, friendship) are expressed in the sexual function. All these sexual associations have in common the fact that on the part of the woman no personal contact, no emotional incentive, exists, and that she does, or suffers, the whole thing from extrasexual motives. However different, unselfish, or conventionally moral this self-surrender may be, it is a form of sexual activity which in principle, in its essential character, must be defined as prostitution.

Compared with these two types of prostitutes, only a

small third group is driven on to the streets by economic distress. These women can be easily recognized by the amateurishness with which they conduct their business; but one must assume that they too suffer from a defect in their personality which permits them to choose this easy way out of their difficulties.

What, now, are the characteristics of a sexual association with a prostitute? They are mainly three: First of all, *Anonymity:* these girls have no face that can be recognized, no name that will be remembered, just a body; they have no emotions, just technique; no individuality, just a trade. Secondly, the relation to *Time:* the association with a prostitute is restricted to the moment when it takes place. It has no extension in time and is wholly unrelated to the future. The fragment of time he spends with a prostitute is completely cut out of a man's life, as a time gap in which nothing significant happened. The third feature is lack of *Significance,* a corollary or result of the previous two: a minute before the man did not know that this woman existed, a minute afterwards he has forgotten that she existed, no trace is left, unchanged he turns away. All these three characteristics indicate that something has happened below the level of specifically human existence, and that those who took part in it lived and acted on this low level, the woman as well as the man.

If we now inquire what kind of men frequent prostitutes, we can distinguish three groups of customers.

The most interesting, practically most important, and from several points of view the most controversial, group are the adolescents.

We must remember that the two component parts of our sexuality, the physical and the emotional, develop for a long time on separate lines which only slowly converge. The physical urge finds its first relief in wet dreams and in the primitive form of masturbation. Later on, during adolescence, this urge is no longer purely endogenous, but is aroused by the female body. The prostitute, who, as we have seen, is a body without a soul, caters for this desire. Moreover, an entirely impersonal contact makes it possible for the beginner to learn the technique of the difficult art of love-making. And as the concept of prostitutes includes women of widely varying personal and social standards, the young man may learn not only the elements of sexual "reading and writing," as it were, but also all the subtleties and refinements of virtuosity.[1]

To this an objection may be raised. Elsewhere in my writing I stated with great emphasis that physical sexuality is, or should be, only the expression of a personal relation. This is true, but it must also be remembered that this psychophysical fusion is the characteristic of mature exemplary sexuality. And here we are dealing with adolescents laboriously groping toward maturity. It may even be admitted that the ideally normal young man finds the way to his personal partner in one great sweep of love and sensuality, but this ideal postulate is in real life swamped by the flood of exceptions. That may be deplorable, but deploring never alters facts. We face here a psychological situation very similar to the homosexuality of youth; intercourse with prostitutes is a step in development, although not an inevitable one; it is a

[1]Some of these girls seem to be less willing to accept their "mission" than they are conscious of their rights as women. One day a man who was already partly advanced in the treatment of his impotence related rather perplexedly this experience. In order to test his progress, he picked up a prostitute, explained his situation, and asked for her assistance—which she refused haughtily, pointing out that she was not a schoolmarm and that she wanted real men. Even she!

halfway solution to a problem which many—and by no means only the abnormal—young men find too difficult to solve in one leap.

But there is still another aspect of our problem. One may ask what is there to be learned. Is there not the instinct of copulation and procreation which guides the first steps of young people on this slippery path? I think the people most competent to answer this question are the many young wives whose marriages are in danger of being wrecked by the total ignorance and incompetence of their "innocent" husbands. True there is a sexual instinct, but we must never forget that nothing in human life is accomplished by instinct alone, and that the sexual instinctive urge in particular is closely interwoven into the vast complex of "human relationships" from which it receives guidance and protection. Furthermore, it is one of the defects of civilization that the unity of personal life is being disrupted, and the dislocated instinct either goes astray or must be redirected by the intellect: this new, and in a way artificial, combination of instinct and intellect is what I call "technique."[2]

The service prostitutes render to the adolescent, and

[2]It may be worth pointing out that by civilization I do not mean the equivalent of a Mayfair mentality in capitals or big towns. It is a form of existence permeating and molding every detail of life. I had the opportunity of watching two generations growing up in a village high up in the Austrian mountains, and saw the people there wrestling with all the problems and conflicts dealt with in psychopathology. An official body of research workers recently investigated Miami County, Ohio, U.S.A., and found that from 10 to 20 per cent of the residents ought to see a psychiatrist. One elementary school-child in five was "seriously maladjusted"; by the time they reached the sixth grade their neurosis was showing. Neuroses were much more common among the poor and ill-educated than among the well-educated. Almost any county in Ohio is considered representative of similar communities in the U.S.A. as a whole.

through him to society, is to teach him the technique of sex life and to offer themselves as a training ground. The impersonal character of this kind of association is essential for this purpose, because any emotional contact would interfere with the unconcernedness with anything but the mere action. And this practical training is indispensable for the satisfactory performance of the complex act of making love. Nothing is more frustrating to the expression of emotion than the incongruity between the wealth of emotions one wants to express and the inadequate command of the means of expression—as every creative or reproducing artist knows. Of course it is not this educational benefit which the young man seeks, but physical relief and pleasure, and one may attribute it to the cunning of Nature that, however unwittingly, he gets so much more.

The second group of the prostitute's customers is composed of neurotics. They are, biologically at least, grown-ups. But fear, the central phenomenon of the neurotic mentality, holds them back from entering into a proper, personal, complete relationship with women. Contact and union mean to them surrender and captivity. They mistake giving themselves for giving themselves up or away. Merging with another person means to them losing their own personality. They consider emotions as bait that may lure them into a trap, and they sense danger where we expect happiness. No wonder that these men try to avoid risks and turn to women who offer an association of guaranteed safety. Here again the prostitute comes to their aid: the anonymity and transitoriness of the relation and its indifference to success and failure provide the sense of security which these men need above all.

The third and by far the largest group patronizing

prostitutes is composed of what one may call the ordinary "man in the street." Whereas the adolescent has not yet achieved sexual maturity, and the neurotic is too afraid to attain it, this type of man never does become mature. The poor substance, the primitive and coarse nature of the personality of these men bar them from ever reaching the fusion of mind and body which constitutes the perfect adult sexuality. The body seeks its gratification, the mind wants pleasure, and the spirit weeps. Once more the prostitute supplies all that is required, and this type of man is the genuine consumer of her wares. The counterpart of these primitives are the oversophisticated men. I said before that the term "prostitute" must not be confined to the girls who make a precarious living from their trade, but that the mentality of prostituting oneself, for whatever purpose, pervades our whole society. This verdict applies to men as well in various ways, and I mean not so much that they prostitute themselves, which often enough they do, as their whole way of living. These socialites who rush from one party to another are incapable of grasping, and therefore establishing, real human relationships, and seek only ephemeral and impersonal contacts, and their sexual contacts are often of the same kind and order.

If one ponders over the psychology of prostitutes and of the men who frequent them, one may come to think that God, or Providence, or whoever may be responsible for this sort of thing, has created this type of defective woman for the express purpose of being a match for the three types of defective men.

12.
Climacteric: The Critical Age in the Male

by Gregorio Marañon, M.D.

The existence of a transitional stage in the life of men that corresponds to the "change of life" in women has been the subject of considerable controversy. From a vast clinical experience, this renowned Spanish specialist concluded that "the climacteric or critical age is . . . a necessary phenomenon in the evolution of every human being who reaches old age, be it man or woman." It is interesting to note that, as Professor Marañon points out in his Preface, there is more literature on almost any rare disease than on the problem of menopause, which comes up every day in the practice of most physicians. This material on the male climacteric, slightly edited for the lay reader, is taken from a comprehensive medical textbook by Dr. Marañon, late Professor of Medical Pathology, Madrid General Hospital. Reprinted from *The Climacteric* by George Marañon, M.D., copyright, 1929, by The C. V. Mosby Company, by permission of the publisher.

See also Chapter 12 in *Women*: "Menopause: The 'Change of Life.'"

THE FIRST QUESTION WHICH ARISES in studying this last aspect of *the critical age* is whether there really exists in the man a period of evolution which may be so described, a period similar to that occuring in woman's life and upon which I have commented at such length in the preceding chapters. Many writers have accepted this idea considering it chiefly from the psychiatric point of view. But others, among them Krafft-Ebing and Vinay, deny it. "To establish a menopause," says the first, "for the

masculine sex, and to particularize the psychoses which
are attached to this age (fifty to sixty years) does not
seem to me admissible from either the biologic or the
clinical point of view." Vinay adds "the masculine menopause is not a fact. It appears to be rather the result of
the imagination of the writers who have described it."

For myself I boldly assert the existence of *the critical
age in the male*. Of the "critical age" I say, and not of
"the menopause," as Krafft-Ebing, Vinay and others say.
Such an expression implies an initial error since evidently the "menopause," the "cessation of the menstrual
flow," is something absolutely alien to the masculine sex.
But in this work we have tried to understand the critical
age, not as a genital episode, not as an incident of the
sexual life more or less accompanied by reactional symptoms on the part of the other apparatus of the economy;
but as a stage of organic evolution, perfectly characterized, anatomically and physiologically, in whose center
the extinction of active genital life stands out prominently, yet not limited to this genital extinction. The line
described by the human organism from birth to death is
not suddenly broken into abrupt descents, like steps. It
is rather a smooth, curved line divided into distinct sectors whose limits are not precise. There are three such
vaguely defined but actual sectors. One embraces the
beginning—infancy. Another takes in the last—old age.
Between these, in the middle, lies full maturity. Now
between these three sectors there are two others, stages
of transition, which are intermediate. In the first the line
is inclined toward the fullness of the curve. This intermediate sector is characterized by the appearance of sexual activity—adolescence. The second intermediate sector
joins the fullness of the curve to the last sector. With
this second intermediate sector the curve of the line be-

gins its descent and this period is characterized by extinction of the sexual function—the climacteric. Adolescence has been rightly called the first critical age, because it is characterized by the same functional instability we have just seen in the climacteric or the second critical age.

The climacteric or critical age is, then, a necessary phenomenon in the evolution of every human being who reaches old age, be it man or woman. The biologic foundation of the feminine climacteric—genital decadence and secondary neuroendocrine reactions—also exist in the male. The different somatic and functional conditions of each sex explain the clinical differences which the critical episode has in the man and in the woman.

CHARACTERISTICS OF THE MASCULINE CLIMACTERIC

The masculine episode comes, indeed, much later than the feminine. It is of more diffuse evolution and limits, as it lacks the menopausal phenomenon as a point of reference. Its organic symptomatology is more attenuated. Its psychologic characteristics are as different from those of the feminine climacteric as the significance of sexual life in man is different from that in woman.

I shall consider first the endogenous and exogenous reasons which justify these differences. Then, from the clinical point of view, I shall detail these symptomatic differences, principally those in the psychic field.

ENDOCRINE CONDITIONS. TESTICULAR INSUFFICIENCY

We know that the endocrine crisis of the climacteric is characterized in the woman by ovarian insufficiency and the secondary reaction of the endocrines and of the nervous-vegetative system. *In the man all these organs react in a much less abrupt way. The reactions are milder* and have qualitative differences which I shall indicate.

However, *testicular insufficiency, the central part of the masculine climacteric, is produced much more slowly and much later than is ovarian insufficiency.* In the majority of cases, in the brief course of a few months the woman passes from full ovarian activity to complete cessation. This occurs within a fixed period—between the forty-fifth and the fifty-fifth year. While in the man, *genital extinction occurs in a more prolonged way and during a much longer space of time.* Very often a man passes the fiftieth year with good sexual aptitude. He may reach seventy, or even exceed that age, with the internal secretion of the testicle intact. I knew a man of seventy-four who cohabited normally twice a week. Cases are frequent where the menopause brings to a wife instinctive and psychic desire for sexual separation while the husband of the same or greater age is still active sexually. Even in cases where the man is unable to perform the sexual act perhaps because of lack of power in the external genital apparatus, difficulty in erection, the internal testicular secretion may not be deficient. The finding of active spermatozoa in the semen of old men up to ninety-one years (Pavlov, cited by Metchnikoff), and one hundred and three (Metchnikoff), shows the prolonged persistence of this secretion until very advanced ages at which the sexual act itself has become impossible. This finding also explains the frequency with which amorous feelings are kept alive in the very old. This same author recalls that "doctors in asylums for the aged have observed that the principal occupation of the patients is discussion of the love question." Although, as we shall see presently, in these late manifestations of libido the psychic element takes part in a preponderant manner and not the sexual instinct properly speaking.

LESSER INTENSITY OF THE THYROID REACTION IN THE MAN

The thyroid reaction, so important in the feminine climacteric, is much less marked in the masculine. In woman the thyroid has a functional excitability, a tendency to instability, which it does not have in man. Hence, in the latter, the lively and characteristic manifestations of hyperthyroid or dysthyroid background alone or combined with the other glandular disturbances will be lacking. These we studied in the menopause, the violent flushes of heat, palpitations, tachycardia, sweating and so forth. We may expect none of them in the masculine climacteric.

However, climacteric hyperthyroidism may also appear in the male, *being characterized especially by loss of weight and psychic symptoms,* especially the latter. Therefore its possible presence in men of this age should not be forgotten, though always less probable than in woman, in those cases of loss of weight which are generally attributed to neurasthenia.

SUPRARENAL REACTION. HYPOPHYSEAL REACTION

Assuming a suprarenal reaction in the feminine sex, the manifestations which are attributed to it will be encountered and perhaps with equal intensity in the male. These are: (1) *Increase in weight.* The masculine figure loses its youthful grace and becomes corpulent, at first pleasing in appearance, later frankly heavy. (2) *The accentuation of masculine hypertricosis.* I have found this phenomenon to be almost constant but writers do not call attention to it. On leaving the third decade the beard and mustache are apt to become heavier, but the symptom is manifested chiefly in the bodily hair, on the chest, forearms, and legs. This grows more thickly or appears for the first time in those individuals who did not have it before. *Note that this is an accentuation of masculine sexual characteristics, in contrast to what occurs in woman. In her the glandular reaction (suprarenal?) of the climacteric acts heterosexually,* that is, tending to transform the feminine morphology into the masculine. (3) *Arterial hypertension,* as constant as in the feminine and perhaps even higher in the masculine sex. This may be because the exogenous factors which collaborate in the production of hypertension are more commonly present in men, such as syphilis, the use of tobacco, overwork and like factors. For these same reasons we are to be guarded in attributing hypertension in women to the climacteric phenomenon alone.

Probably the *hypophyseal reaction* also intervenes in the climacteric crisis in the man. In rare cases this gives rise to acromegalic syndromes, more frequently to the peculiar adiposities with which we are now familiar and which I shall mention again, and perhaps in advanced years to senile atrophy.

Exogenous Circumstances Which Influence the Development of the Critical Age in the Male

The exogenous circumstances are also different in the man. *Certain pathologic processes are more frequently displayed than in the woman. These act preferably on the circulatory system, and, either through that medium or directly, on the nervous system.* Such are some infections, as syphilis, alcoholic or nicotine intoxication, emotional excesses, overfatigue, and so forth, all of which explains the intensity of, and the greater proportion of, insanity as manifested in men. On the other hand, as a consequence of his sexual characteristics, upon which I shall dwell later, man finds this period one of increased possibility through his business or professional activity. This balances and compensates the decline in primary sexual activity. Even after this age the height of man's business or professional activity sometimes persists. Legrand,[1] to speak of only one of the many examples, mentions those men who, past sixty, arrive at the very peak of their respective capacities. The World War gave us a remarkable lesson as to the social value of old men, of whom, among others can be cited Foch, Joffre, Giolitti, Hindenburg, and Clemenceau. In women, on the contrary, the loss of sexual power implies a radical, physiologic change, as I have indicated.

PECULIARITIES OF CRITICAL SYMPTOMATOLOGY IN THE MAN. GENITAL SYMPTOMS

Thus we see that the symptomatology of the masculine climacteric presents peculiarities as compared to the feminine. The *genital symptoms* in the man are very simple. The erectile power of the external genital apparatus progressively diminishes until it is completely lost. This is accompanied by flaccidity and slow atrophy of the penis and testicles, darkening of the scrotum, and uncurling of the pubic hair. These phenomena are often effected parallel to a diminution of the sexual impulse and therefore without psychic disharmony. Less often the amorous appetite persists, giving rise to a state of

[1]Legrand: *La longevité à travers les ages.* Paris, 1911.

sad resignation in the climacteric man or his instinct goes astray toward more or less complex sexual aberrations. A state of semierection may last many years and be adequate for normal, orderly amorous relation. Certain affections of the urinary apparatus proper to this age, such as prostatitis, may create a state of local irritation favorable to erectile power and priapism without libido. I have seen some such cases.

* * * * * * * * * * * * * *

PSYCHOLOGY OF THE CRITICAL AGE IN MAN. THE EMOTIONAL INSTABILITY OF MATURITY

I have intentionally kept for the last a consideration of *the psychic sphere,* because here we find the symptoms which especially characterize the crisis of the sexual subsidence in the man. Following my method of commenting upon these manifestations in the feminine menopause, I shall consider first the *"elemental psychologic disturbances"* of the climacteric, and later the *psychopathies properly speaking.*

Emotional instability is a frequent characteristic of the psychology of man in this age, only it is presented with rather less intensity than in woman. In her the reactions dependent on the endocrino-vegetative system are always more violent, at least in their external expression. The emotional sphere of man has apparently been rendered dormant by his struggle for existence, but at this age he is apt to reach his maximum emotional susceptibility. Such men have told me that they were now moved emotionally by things to which they were formerly indifferent.[2] Great fighters, of little sentiment in the

[2]In my essay on Age and Emotion I referred to this phenomenon in speaking of woman's climacteric loss of emotional control. There I

early part of life, become gentler, more understanding, and indulgent in the period of decline. Maturity is also the time for the conversion of great sinners.[3] And to this the climacteric instability of the endocrino-vegetative emotional system contributes very largely.

CLIMACTERIC IMPATIENCE, INSTABILITY IN MAN

Impatience, becoming easily exasperated, is a very frequent sign of loss of emotional control in the climacteric man, as in the woman. Many men of uniform and tran-

copied these lines, more expressive than any description, from a letter sent me by a well-known writer who was rounding the cape of the fifty-fifth year in rough weather:

"My eyes fill with tears, a sob escapes me, my throat tightens easily now, only on seeing a child, hearing a musical note or seeing a misfortune. Now I move my hearers when lecturing, for my soul is hypersensitive through force of suffering, deception, and struggle. And from this exaggerated sentimentalism I gather much deep consolation."

[3]In proof of this note the frequency with which conversion coincides with an emotional state, either a sudden and exciting emotion, like Paul's vegetative terror at the lightning during the tempest, or the Duke of Gandia's sentimental horror on seeing the Empress Isabel converted into a hideous mass. It may be gentle, like an altruistic action or spiritual words, or merely solitude in a beautiful landscape. Such was the critical moment of St. Augustine's conversion. About the year 386 he stood—after an unfortunate youth—upon the threshold of maturity. Following a period of internal struggle which not only agitated his spirit but also his body, "animated by unfamiliar emotions" he fled to solitude and "being under a fig tree" beneath the Italian sky in the latter part of autumn he suddenly felt "two streams of tears gush from his eyes." St. Augustine, so attentive to the details of his inner life, makes no allusions in all his *confessions* to nature other than this detail of the fig tree. Here we find revealed how emotion inspired by nature about him was linked to his spiritual crisis. This feeling inspired by nature is one of the finest and most suggestive possessed by the human spirit and serves as a steppingstone to important emotional states.

quil character throughout life become impatient, irritable, and violent in this age. The usual little cares of the home or profession which before were scarcely noticed, now constitute a torment. This change is readily perceived at home and abroad. The explanation of the phenomenon is always the same, emotional irritability. Naturally the psychic states related directly or indirectly to sexual decadence have a large influence upon the characteristic irritability of some men in this age.

Disturbances of Sexual Feeling. Pathologic Lessening of Libido

The *disturbances of sexual feeling* properly speaking are less interesting than in the feminine menopause, for the reasons so often explained. The *lessening of the sexual impulse* rarely reaches pathologic limits, being brought about in a more gradual manner with less shock than in the woman. It also occurs much later. I did see, however, a patient who, on reaching fifty experienced an almost abrupt loss of libido with voluntary renunciation of all sexual relation. Here is a state similar, although with more marked intervention on the part of the purely psychic elements, those which I described in previous chapters as occurring in women.

Rarity of Sexual Melancholy in the Man

The symptom which I called *sexual melancholy*, so complex and so interesting in the other sex, is of very little importance in man. Organically the depressive commotion which causes the suppression of the genital hormones is less in the man than in the woman, since in him the primary genital function is less important than in her. Moreover its extinction is accomplished in a less brusque manner and covers a much longer period of time. Nor is the loss of sexual power apt to be followed psychically by the depressive states which are observed in the woman. This is because of the lesser significance which this loss has in masculine psychology, and because it coincides with the fullness of business or professional activity. This not only is an efficacious consolation, but, according to my way of thinking, represents a certain kind of sexual (parasexual) satisfaction in the man.

The states of *"sexual melancholy"* are, then, very rare in normal climacteric man. We find only isolated examples, in those subjects of Don Juan temperaments. These I consider as of ambiguous sexual psychology. I might mention two or three cases which I have collected of true melancholia in the face of physical ruin in men of this sexual context. I copy as typical a description taken from a novel by E. Montfort[4] which is scarely true literally, but very interesting from this point of view. The hero, a ladies' man, surprised and disillusioned on entering his fortieth year meditates thus: "Forty years! He was forty years old! His age was written in every bit of him, in the flabbiness of his face, in the heaviness of his body, while his heart, not aged but still young, beat as though it were at its twenty-fifth year. Forty years! Pleasure was ended, no longer could he interest women. Having reached the end of youth, having passed the time of love, what pleasure in life now remained to him? The obsession of the lost paradise, the thought of things past, the ever present memory of the enchanted country where he had once been and whither he can never more return! All is lost at this age." And later: "He beheld himself in

[4] E. Montfort: *La belle-enfant ou l'amour à 40 ans.* Paris, 1918.

a mirror. The image was terrible. Impossible to retain the least illusion that he was the same being. He saw the whole disagreeable transformation, his wrinkles, the crow's-feet they had made in his cheeks, the flabbiness of his skin, his thick neck. He was withered, worn out. He was old. Fifteen years before he had seen a man of about this age go out of the house and he now recalled exactly the impression which he had produced, the painful sense of physical ruin, a potbellied being in a shirt, disheveled, his eyes swollen, his legs hairy. The spectacle had been grotesque and lamentable. And now he himself was like that man."

The lamentation of this Don Juan, evidently abnormal in his sexual make-up, could not be less masculine. The author adds later with a certain sagacity, "He was inconsolable. Stronger men, less effeminate characters, those whose existence is more active, accept physical decadence. They pay some attention to it. They suffer, perhaps, upon the appearance of the first wrinkle, when the first hair falls out, when abdominal fat begins, but they suffer in only a transient way. By the side of loss they can write gain. Maturity of spirit, more complete possession of themselves, intellectual and moral benefit compensate them for the physical loss."

The Age of Love in the Modern Man. Social Well-Being as an Element of Sexual Attraction

The abnormality and the rarity of these forms of sexual melancholy in the man are accentuated in modern times. It is evident that in present-day society, correctly reflected in the amatory conflicts of contemporary drama and fiction, the lover is of a more mature type than were the gallants of the classic and romantic eras. Toulouse[5] says truly, "around the age of forty, the age of gray hair wherein Molière's Arnolphe became ridiculous to the ladies, our contemporaries have made the greatest distraction in the feminine heart." "In the theater of today," he adds, "the 'young gallant' is frequently a man in the close of life."

The backward transition of the age of love in man is due to complex causes which I cannot develop here. On one side, it is evident that humanity has taken into account that the concept of youth which has been accepted for centuries—or to put it better, the granted supremacy of youth—rests on entirely superficial foundations, and this concept is beginning to be rectified. The young man is, no doubt, more handsome, more agile and has neither wrinkles nor gray hair. He bears certain physical attacks with difficulty and as yet has not the idea of responsibility which sharpens the actions of the mature man. But none of this upholds the essential superiority of youth. The genital function, subject in youth to weaknesses dangerous at times to later life, does not reach its full stability until the thirty-fifth year or later. Resistance to physical work and above all to intellectual work does not reach its maximum until about fifty. The amount of rest required by youth is less and material necessities much more limited. Emotional life is, as we have seen, of very late apogee, and intellectual control is also fuller and more refined when the youth comes to bear a considerable number of years upon his shoulders.[6]

[5]Toulouse: *La question sexuelle et la femme*. Paris, 1918. See also: Vorvenel: *La crépuscule de l'esprit;* Mercure de France. Mar. 15, 1924. He cites numerous modern books wherein the hero is very mature.

[6]This statement is not incompatible with the theory sustained by many writers and particularly by Ostwald in his well-known volume

Why, then, has this overwhelming superiority of middle age in the noblest human activities not created a concept of a "golden age" which should depose this present concept based on purely morphologic elements? It would be most interesting to investigate why youth has maintained itself for so many centuries as an age uniquely desirable—and does so continue in spite of changes which are beginning.

I have discussed this elsewhere at a length improper here. But I may point out that youth's panegyric has been written since the beginning of the world by the old. And the old do not weigh the advantages and the inconveniences of each age at their individual and specific value; but rather in their relation to a phenomenon which, consciously or unconsciously, is projected upon human thought since it ends it—death. When youth is extolled over the years which follow, it is not youth in general that enchants us but our own lost youth. It is not the vigor, the joy, the youthful freedom from care for which we envy this age. It is rather the mere fact of its being the farthest removed from our own death. If human life developed inversely and the mature man dissolved like a snowball melting in the sun, to end in the unicellular germ, who can doubt that these same longings, now applied to youth and childhood, would be applied to maturity and old age?

Les grandes hommes (Dufour's French edition, Paris, 1912) as to the precocity with which the majority of great men are apt to produce the fruits of their genius. Besides these early geniuses there are late ones like Cervantes, Pasteur, and many others. Moreover, discovery and invention, which is what Ostwald refers to principally, is often favored by impulsive activity, by the very lack of critical talent in youth. But the whole work, developed, clarified, and conscious, the work rather of pedagogy and social diffusion, is apt to be late even in these precocious inventors.

But when the value of each stage is judged without this unconscious projection of feeling toward one's own life, then certainly youth is not the most to be desired. A man seeking a collaborator in the most noble human enterprises, one to direct people or industries or financial projects—the sick man seeking a physician, another seeking a counsellor—all value maturity above youth. When the young achieve these high positions it is because a premature equilibrium has enabled them to reach the excellencies of maturity aforetime. And this same criterion, this preference for the more mature may have an influence in the choice of a mate.

The fact is that the incidence of marriage between young women and men already mature is constantly increasing. A large majority of women agree with the line of thought expressed by Pérez de Ayala:

"A man's heart does not acquire full capacity for love and for every delicate or passionate sentiment until between the fortieth and fiftieth years. . . . Then man is more seductive than at any other time."

It is clear that in the phenomenon we are discussing there is doubtless a material motive, whose consideration we should not overlook. Of course the mature man's economic and social position is stronger, or at least better assured, than it was in his youth. How then, shall we judge a woman who "marries for money," in the common phrase? I believe that we should be far less severe than society, hypocritically, has been. I leave out of consideration those women who, violating every emotional, moral and esthetic sense, marry degenerate, physically repugnant men, whom they despise, solely for money. These we need not consider. But the woman who, on feeling intensely drawn to a man, reflects on his poverty and even lets this fact weigh heavily in her decision, is

she as contemptible as these others? I say no. A man's
social status has a sexual value, as I have already explained. His business or professional success is therefore
a means of sexual attraction. Money, like glory, is the
practical expression of that success. Therefore the influence which a large fortune, like that of social position,
exercises upon a woman seeking a mate may be adjudged
a legitimate biologic means of attraction. Often, as we
know, money does not represent any social success, being
merely an inert inheritance. But even so the possession
of a large fortune gives a certain social preponderance,
secondary but unquestionable. To triumph one must be
rich. But being rich one may triumph easily. In every
case the possession of money is a necessary element to
fulfill the fundamental instinct for maternity. It may
not have been so formerly, but it is so now and money
is becoming more and more necessary. Gold now approaches the class of elements which are not yet of primal
necessity but which are radical, biologic necessities like
health. A woman may be a mother without money, as
she can be a mother without health, but in an imperfect
way. These ideas, which I developed in the first edition
of this text, are becoming more commonly accepted.
There is an extensive social justification for them as the
economic difficulties of life become more acute. Prévost,[7]

7M. Prévost: *Nouvelles lettres à Françoise ou la jeune fille d'après
guerre*, Paris, 1924. In fact Schopenhauer sustained this same thesis in
commenting on the Spanish proverb "who marries for love must live
with grief." "The contrary happens" he says "when we consider marriages of convenience, governed by family interest." Schopenhauer,
however, was mistaken, in my opinion, in assuming that money is
prejudicial to the species. On the contrary, the species is just what
gains when there is no lack of money in the home. The woman who
marries for money sacrifices her own happiness for the good of her
offspring. The great philosopher of Dantzig remarks that in that

in a study of the present-day woman, exactly expresses these ideas in the words he puts into the mouth of a young woman. She had repulsed a man who was pleasing to her on being informed that he had no fortune:

"Nothing I said is extraordinary. If I knew there was an hereditary disease in his family, however little it was his fault, everyone would find my coldness very natural. The lack of fortune is likewise a tare among the wheat. He is somewhat incomplete and unsound. This is the way I think—and many others do, too."

Economic equilibrium, then, becomes a point of sexual attraction. And in general, this equilibrium is reached only in postjuvenile years, when the chronologic field of masculine sexual suggestion is considerably widened.

This inclination of young women toward mature men at times finds a corresponding phase in the attraction which young women have for many men who have reached the age of sexual subsidence.

Man's Feeling of Being Left Behind Socially, Equivalent to Sexual Melancholy in Woman

But on the other hand, in the climacteric man there is frequently a psychic state which we may consider as equivalent to "sexual melancholy" in the woman. This is *the sense of being ill-used, left behind* or *prematurely forgotten* by the coming generations. This psychic state

analytic glance with which young men and women scrutinize each other on meeting for the first time there is felt the genius of the species which is evaluating each. Now no doubt there enters into the meditation of this genius along with a consideration of the psychic and physical qualities of the possible lovers a gauging of the economic resources of each.

which embitters the existence of many men in the decline
is presented as a plain psychopathic manifestation in
varying grades from simple worry, compatible with normal conditions, up to true states of *persecutory delirium*.
It may be combined with psychopathies properly speaking—melancholia and so forth—which I shall consider
later. Each age has its place in life. The same is true of
sexual activity which is as important in woman's life as
social or business activity is fundamental in the sexually
balanced man's life. Normal men and women keep this
in mind and adapt themselves naturally to the passing
moment. But if the nervous system is unbalanced by the
rude struggle for existence or by previous diseases, on
reaching the critical age with its exquisite emotional
sensitiveness the spirit rebels in the face of the natural
descent. In the woman this rebellion gives rise to "sexual
melancholy" and in the man to its biologic equivalent,
suspiciousness in the presence of the natural advance of
youth which is always turbulent and iconoclastic.

EVOLUTION TOWARD CONSERVATISM

In this connection it is curious to note the evolution
toward conservatism which normally occurs in the man
in his social activity the sexual character of which I have
so stressed. Man's social activity results from the counter-
posed action of two orders of impulses, one excitant, the
other inhibitory. This is true, indeed, of all organic
functions. Now many of these functions, like metabolism,
growth, sexual libido, and so forth, in the course of life
undergo a rather fixed evolution which is characterized
by the predominance of the excitant elements during
youth, by their balance during middle age, and by the
predominance of the inhibitory elements during organic

decline. Social activity, despite its complexity, follows a parallel evolution. In youth the impulses which we may call centrifugal are altruistic, correspond to the impulsive, unorganized intellectual power and to the lack of autocriticism and the aptitude for those emotions I have called "epic" or of "large vibration." These are the impulses which give rise in science to great discoveries, in art to reformations frequently and in politics to advanced policies and propaganda. These movements are considered by contemporaries as revolutionary. But when this age passes, and parallel to the evolution of the metabolism and the organic morphology itself of the different general functions, then the inhibitory impulses, centripetal, egoistic, begin to prevail over the centrifugal. The sense of responsibility is increased, the affectivity is sensitized to the "lyric" emotions or those of "small vibration." The man, in short, whatever his occupation, tends to strip from his work the audacious and aggressive character of youth. He becomes *conservative*. In studying humanity one of the most conspicuous things is the unfailing repetition of this phenomenon of conservative transformation in each individual and in each generation, always provoking the same surprise and protest from the rising generation. This evolution is regarded as a childish desertion due to egotism or as due to organic decadent diffidence. It is not seen to be the inevitable course of a complex function as linked to the evolution of the individual as are the more simple vegetative functions. Nor is it ever thought to be probable that we all shall follow a like evolution which has gone on repeating itself without interruption as far back as man has a history.

Of course in stating that an evolution toward conservatism occurs in every individual I am not speaking in a

strict sense. There are, indeed, men who remain inno-
vators in social activity up to very advanced age. There
are many examples of artists, scientists and statesmen
who accomplish their revolutionary work after fifty, at
times in full old age. But these are always geniuses, exceptional men. Moreover, in these it is easy to show the
presence of an uncommon organic energy and, above
all, a persistency of sexual activity which exceeds the law
of time. These demonstrate nothing contrary to my
thesis. The inhibitory conservative impulses do not appear until very late because sexual evolution, the axis of
the principal functions, is very late.[8]

PATHOLOGIC INCREASE OF SEXUAL FEELING. DISHARMONY WITH GENITAL CAPACITY AND ITS CONSEQUENCES

Pathologic increase of sexual feeling is rather frequent
in the climacteric man. In general it assumes different
forms than in woman, since not all the organic and
psychic reasons which explain the frequency of this
pathologic condition in climacteric woman are applicable to man. In the latter it is almost exclusively a phenomenon of purely psychic origin and nature. *Its characteristic is disharmony between the increase of sexual
appetite and the diminution of power in the genital
organs.* Men are rare in whom libido does not survive
erectile power. This lack of parallelism between the impulse and the functional capacity does not exist in
woman because of her passive attitude in the sexual act.
But in man the active element is very important. In this
phenomenon should be sought the cause of many psycho-

[8]Likewise, in any class of activity conservatism in youth is an indication of a precarious vital energy, of a premature spiritual senility
when not due to a conscious attitude.

sexual phenomena of masculine maturity. Such are, for example, the *abnormal, perhaps aberrant, forms of sexual gratification,* the attainment of which forces some to break the calm rules of their usual life. The most frequent of these abnormal forms is the *gerocomic tendency;* that is, desire for very young girls. At times this reaches grades of pathologic intensity, of true exhibitionism in men of previous circumspect habits. I could cite various personal observations of this tendency in individuals, some of whom have acquired newspaper notoriety.

Another Consequence of This Hypersensual-Hypogenital Disharmony; the Social Submission of Man to Woman

Another very interesting effect of this disharmony is the *social submission of man to woman.* The sexually normal man walks through life at his own pace, followed by the woman. His respect for feminine will is limited to the occasions when he has to overcome the resistance of the woman to the primary sexual act. But, except within very narrow limits, her sway does not extend to his life beyond this circle. *Outside the home no normal man is the slave of the woman,* however ardent and secure may be the spiritual and passionate tie which unites them. This does not exclude, naturally, the reality of a certain feminine influence always useful and agreeable in special moments in the struggle for existence.[9] What

---

[9]This influence, of secondary type, is founded in part on the value of feminine advice. Woman's conservatism and practical advice well balances the idealistic exaggeration of the man's social efforts. And in part the influence is due to the agreeable voluptuousness which the strong feel in submitting to the caprices of the weak. To this same

I have said in another chapter and again in this one regarding the psychology of sex justifies this statement, while an intimate study of men confirms it in every case. When a man is moved throughout life by the insistent influence of a woman, it is evident that his sexual equilibrium is not perfect. This is absolute when his specific hormones are weak, his genital apparatus defective, or it is relative when the excessive energy of the heterosexual hormones in the woman react on him. Naturally the practical consequence of this disequilibrium, submission in the man, reaches its greatest strength when there is a tie of intense affection on his part which maintains the union with the woman. Such is the case of some men sexually normal during previous years, who on reaching this age of sexual subsidence are urged on by a determined woman, through a psychic exacerbation of the sexual sentiment. Here is the psycho-physiologic conflict favorable for great submission on the part of the man. It has been during this age that the greater number of women who have influenced history, not through their own direct acts but through the instrument of some statesman, have found men docile to their suggestions. A representative type is the well-known hero in Bernstein's *La Griffe*.

ABSENCE OF THE HETEROSEXUAL TENDENCY IN THE CRITICAL AGE OF MAN

As we have seen, in the endocrine crisis of the masculine climacteric the *tendency to sexual inversion,* so common and typical in the feminine, is much less frequent.

phenomenon is due the domination of children who at times, as in so many sentimental tales, conquer men of indomitable will and character.

In nonpathologic conditions, revivification of the hetero-sexual secondary characteristics does not occur with the same regularity as in woman. But at times, on the contrary, there is a reinforcement of masculine characteristics. For this biologic reason the inversive tendency, likely to occur in the climacteric woman, does not have so great an importance in the crisis in man. However, late manifestations of homosexualism may coincide with this period of life, at times leading to manifestations which are scandalous. It is possible that the predilection for very young women felt by men in sexual decadence, the "gerocomic tendency" of which I spoke, is really a dissimulated homosexual inclination localized in the ambiguous, androgynous type of girl very close to puberty.

Psychopathies Properly Speaking

The *psychopathies, properly speaking,* of the masculine climacteric have been well studied. . . . All agree that in man, as compared to woman, these are apt to be of greater intensity, doubtless because of the greater frequency and energy with which toxic and venereal infections act, directly or indirectly, through the medium of the circulation. For the rest, the description I gave in considering the feminine menopause is, with the exception of the usual pathologic differences in the sexes, applicable to man.

The most characteristic affection is *involutional melancholia.* This is presented with considerable frequency in climacteric man, with all the characteristics I have described and with its varying termination, favorable in some cases, unfavorable in others. Perhaps the latter is more frequent than in women, through its readier continuity with the arteriosclerotic dementias.

The different *paranoias* mentioned as occurring in women are also presented in the other sex. Cases of religious delirium are not rare. I have seen several very typical cases in some of which the men stood high socially. The same is true of *sexual deliriums and aberrations, persecutory delirium, pathologic envy,* and so forth. All these states are the prolongation of the psychic abnormalities which we have studied in the preceding pages.

NEURASTHENIA AND THE CRITICAL AGE IN MAN

Among the neuroses, neurasthenia has been described, chiefly by Regis, as very frequent and persistent. But now we know that many of the cases so diagnosed are, as I set forth in speaking of the feminine neuroses, true states of involutional melancholia or of the initial disturbances of presenile dementia, as Regis states.

But in other cases the condition is really *genuine physical and psychic exhaustion,* the "*run-down*" state as it is phrased, corresponding to the old idea of neurasthenia, without psychopathic disturbance properly speaking. Yet this state corresponds to the psychologic characteristics of the climacteric which have already been enumerated. The symptoms are quieted by rest, but quickly reappear on the least physical effort and especially on any mental or emotional effort. They are aggravated after cohabitation and are accompanied often by hyperthyroid symptomatology which slowly but finally disappears. I have seen several cases coinciding exactly with this description. As characteristic I copy a clinical history, written by the patient himself.

CASE 110.—A civil engineer. "I am fifty-six years old. I have always been well, thin and very nervous. I have worked a great deal in my life, and I was passionate about everything, important and unimportant. A year ago I went through a long period of professional worry and annoyance and a little later I began to lose weight without cause for I ate and slept well. Digestion was good. Without knowing why, I was better for some months and regained the lost six kilos of weight. But suddenly I lost them again. They suspected I was diabetic but the urine was always normal at every analysis. At the same time that I lost weight I experienced my nervous disturbances. So sudden were the severe prostrations, so alarming, that I remained in bed all day—they were like nervous excitations. At times the weakness in my legs made me think I was going to fall, that I could not get out of bed. But I rose and by an effort of will went out and worked. It often happened that by night the weariness left me and I worked until dawn. Some days I could only crawl to my office but left it sprightly—as if my body weighed nothing and I were twenty. There were days when everything irritated me and angered me. I do not see how the members of my household and my companions endured me patiently. I also complained of pains like rheumatism, in the sides and shoulders—every day in a different spot. I slept well but before I went to sleep my head and heart throbbed."

Examining the patient some time later I observed: thin type, eyes large and brilliant, tachycardia (pulse 100-110), great vasomotor irritability; great vehemence of movement and expression; hypertension 19 (Riva-Rocci), tremor of the hands, reflexes heightened and symmetrical. Circulatory apparatus and respiration normal. Syphilis, negative. Two years later he was well. Evidently this subject had a constitutionally hyperthyroid temperament and on reaching the climacteric years he suffered an increased hyperthyroidism. This, with the

hypertension and vasomotor reactions of his age, produced a condition of physical and mental asthenia with
very marked irritability, the classic neurasthenic type.[10]

However, I would insist upon considering with caution
the psychopathic disturbances of this age as being purely
functional or psychic and linked to the climacteric episode. My experience of the last few years has taught me
that even in those cases most easily fitting the typical
description of climacteric states, *even in those in which
the symptomatology disappears and mental integrity is
recovered*, there are often pathologic lesions linked to
the arteriosclerotic psychopathies. Indeed, after some
time somatic signs of arteriosclerosis reappear, at times
with greater intensity, it being possible to prove them
in the intervening periods of apparent recovery. This
does not authorize one to say, perhaps, like Bleuler that
the so-called climacteric psychopathies should be eliminated from psychiatric terminology but rather that we
should modify our concept and prognosis of them. I may
sum up my belief in this respect by stating that the climacteric has an influence on the chronology of presenile
and senile psychoses perhaps through the circulatory and
toxic reaction which presumably contributes to their
production. But it has no other influence.

[10]Vorvenel (*Op. cit.*) cites P. Margueritt's observation of himself.
In his novel La Flamme he refers to his own climacteric melancholia,
which is, indeed, very typical. He mentions other men of letters who,
at fifty, are overtaken by a condition of asthenia and disenchantment
causing them to shun society and at times to break off their literary
labors (Shakespeare, Racine, Huysmans, D'Annunzio). These attacks
may be considered as climacteric exhaustion (run-down condition)
except when they were theatrically premeditated.

13.
The Art of Love

by Kenneth Walker, M.D.

In his illuminating discussion of the techniques involved in the physical consummation of love, Dr. Walker avoids both the sentimentality and the antiseptic, pseudoscientific approach of most sex manuals. His one golden rule is that love-making must be spontaneous. To this end, the mutual needs and roles of both partners in every phase of sexual intercourse are clearly and thoroughly explained. Kenneth Walker is a consultant surgeon in London, former Hunterian Professor of the Royal College of Surgeons, and the author of numerous technical works as well as several books for the layman. Reprinted from *Sex in Social Life*, edited by Sybil Neville-Rolfe, copyright, 1950, by W. W. Norton & Company, Inc., by permission of the publisher.

See also Chapters 1, 13 in *Women:* "The Sexual Impulse and the Art of Love," "On Love."

I. WHY LOVE-MAKING MUST BE LEARNED

THERE ARE SOME WHO WOULD DENY that love is an art. They would maintain that it is an instinct, and that love-making can be safely left to a man's and a woman's natural impulses. Why bother to describe what is a natural function? We do not need books to teach us how to eat or drink; nor do we require to be taught how to make love.

But it is in the nature of man to take what is a natural impulse and evolve it to its highest level by the refining force of art. Even what we eat and drink has been submitted to study, and from this study has been evolved the culinary art. So must it be with the natural function of reproduction. The civilized world has long ago realized that it is not enough to rely solely on a woman's maternal instinct for the upbringing of her child. Mothercraft has therefore been studied, and many works are every year published on this subject.

That instruction in love-making is equally necessary will be realized by any of us who has been called upon to deal with the difficulties encountered by men and women in marriage. Not only the technique of love-making but even its fundamental principles are unknown to many newlywed couples. This statement may apply equally well to what are known as the "educated classes" as it does to the great mass of the people. On one occasion the writer was consulted by a solicitor of forty-two who had been married for two years and had come to the conclusion that something was missing from his marriage. He was right. The marriage had never been consummated, and what was more surprising still he had no idea how consummation could be achieved. A solicitor of forty-two had therefore to be instructed in the rudiments of physical love-making. Truly, civilized man is sometimes a more astonishing creature than is the raw savage, and would appear to be more in need of instruction in the art of love than a South Sea Islander.

No excuse need then be offered for the title of this Section. Love is an art and, since it is intimately connected with man's emotions and with the more spiritual side of his nature, an art that is to him of the greatest importance. The mating instinct serves not only to assure the continuance of the race, but also to provide material for the harmonious development of man's personality. In the words of Dr. M. J. Exner, a distinguished American authority on problems of sex and marriage: "It may not be too much to say that while biologically procreation remains the primary function of sex in human life, psychologically its primary function has come to vivify, enrich and develop love. Those who still insist upon animal analogy as a guide for human conduct, holding that sex union is justifiable only for the purpose of procreation, are in fundamental error. They fail to appreciate the great contribution sex has to make to the spiritual life of man. In human beings sex serves the end of love, independent of procreation."

It should be realized that men upon attaining sexual maturity at adolescence, come into full possession of their mating capacity. They are sexually awake and do not require sexual experiences for the development of their powers. With women it is otherwise. In the words of Dunlop, "The development of sexual desire in the woman is far more a matter of education, through sexual stimulation and sexual experience, than is the case with a man. In many women the desire is very slight until developed by repeated stimulations and experiences, and may thereafter be powerful and easily aroused."

There is, however, one objection that may be brought against these chapters with somewhat more justification. Love may be an art, but an art cannot be learnt from a book. No one by reading a work on the violin can straightway become a violinist; no manual on painting can make of one who has never painted an artist. Nor can a book—or, as in this case, a part of a book—on the art of love convert a man or a woman into a skilled lover.

No pretense is made here that it can. All that it is hoped to do is to supply the ordinary man and woman with some initial understanding of the problem before them. Armed with this theoretical knowledge, they will at any rate be in a better position to avoid the pitfalls

which so frequently spell disaster for the entirely unin-
structed. They will be safeguarded from certain mistakes;
they will know how to attempt to overcome certain difficulties. They will at all events have a theoretical knowledge of the subject, a general understanding. Practice
and experience will in time teach them how to use this
knowledge.

That is the utmost that can be effected; and it would
be an error to attempt to achieve more than is possible.
The motive force behind love-making is the emotions,
and the exact way in which these will express themselves
will vary in different individuals. Love-making carried
out in accordance with some set standard gleaned from
a book would be but a meaningless figment. It would
have lost all its spontaneity, be as lacking in individuality
as the movements conned from a drill book. The exact
form in which a husband and wife express their love is
their own concern. It cannot and must not be learned
solely from a book.

By way of introduction to the subject it will first be
advisable to indicate briefly the physical act of love, an
act to which the term coitus has been applied by the
scientists. By this is meant the series of events which
starts with the initial stirrings of sexual desire in the
man and the woman and ends with ejaculation of the
male sexual secretions (semen) within the genital passages of the female.

It must be realized that a mere description of the
physical events of coitus is as incomplete a description
of love-making as would be a word picture of two people
pressing their lips together a true description of affection.
The pressing of lips together is but the outward expression of an intense emotional experience, an experience
which no words are adequate to describe. So also are the

intimacies of physical union the outward expression of an emotional and even spiritual experience that cannot adequately be conveyed in language. Because of this a coldly scientific account of coitus divorced from its psychological accompaniment often seems to sensitive readers a travesty of love; from which they recoil with irritation and even with disgust. This is almost inevitable, and it is difficult to see how it can be avoided, however gifted be the pen of the writer and however conscious he may be of the limitations of his description.

II. THE TECHNIQUE OF SEXUAL UNION

It is impossible to avoid the use of certain scientific terms in a description of sexual intercourse. Many of these have already been explained in the section dealing with the physiology of the sex organs, but it will be as well for the reader to remind himself of their meaning before he embarks upon the following pages. Wherever possible, words in everyday use have been substituted for those employed generally in scientific writings.

By sexual intercourse is meant the full range of contact and connection between a man and woman for sexual consummation. Its biological purpose is the fertilization of the female ovum by the depositing of semen within the female passages, but, as has previously been pointed out, sexual intercourse is as important to the individual as an expression of his love as it is to the race as a means of perpetuating the species. "Every natural faculty, by means of exercise, evolution and inheritance, can become an Art," we are told, and the natural function of impregnation, because it has become so intimately linked with the emotional life of the man and woman, serves the expression of love as faithfully as it serves the purpose of the race.

The material with which love works is the sensations supplied by the special senses of touch, sight, sound and smell. All play their part in the sequence of events that constitute intercourse, the relative importance of each special sense varying somewhat with different individuals and at different times. If an emphasis were to be placed on any one of them it would have to be on the sense of touch, for it is no exaggeration to say that if a man were to be blind and deaf and to have lost the power of smell he would still derive from sexual intercourse its richest impressions.

The Five Phases

In describing sexual intercourse it is customary to divide it into five phases: the prelude, love-play, sexual union, the climax or orgasm, and the epilogue or afterplay. This is a conventional method of presentation, but it must be remembered that the division of intercourse into stages is only for purposes of description. Each phase passes insensibly into the following, and there exist no hard and fast lines of demarcation between them. Intercourse should rather be likened to a piece of music played by two people which starts gently with a prelude, passes with increasing force and speed to its zenith and then gently falls in the "diminuendo" of the afterglow. Each movement merges into the other by delicate gradations, and each may repeat for a short while the "motif" of its predecessor.

The prelude may be said to begin with the first stirrings of sexual desire. The husband looks upon his wife and is made conscious of the attraction that she exerts over him. The wife looks upon her husband and feels within her heart the surge of desire. Erotic thoughts mingle with the sense of attraction. They see each other not only as loving companions but as man and woman, possessing and possessed, divided by a hundred differences yet drawn toward each other by the unifying force of love.

It is impossible to fix on the moment at which this prelude ends and love-play begins, unless we arbitrarily decide that it is the kiss which initiates the second phase. Nevertheless the kiss sometimes mingles with the prelude, for of kisses there are more than one kind. The light momentary contact of two lips with another's cheek is one thing, the erotic kiss is another. The first may well form a part of the prelude, but the lover's kiss may rightfully be taken as marking the beginning of the love-play.

The chief attribute of the erotic kiss is that it is mutual, that it is given and received from mouth to mouth with mutual pressure. The woman or the man who has never loved has never learnt even to kiss; for them kissing has been merely the brushing of another's face with the lips. The erotic kiss is rich in variations. From its lightest form, "the butterfly kiss" it may pass through an infinity of gradations, from the closed to the open lips, to the kiss lasting for many minutes.

It is the part played by the tongue that more particularly distinguishes the friendly from the lover's kiss. Usually this takes the form of the tip of the tongue being protruded between the lips so that it comes into contact with the loved one's tongue or caresses gently her lips.

Occasionally the part played by the tongue is so exaggerated that instead of merely touching the lips it actually explores the other's mouth.

Kisses also vary markedly according to the peculiar tactile sensation imparted, and according to the part

played by the teeth. It is not surprising, therefore, that
the passionate kiss of the lover passes by degrees into
the lover's bite. Possibly this is a relic of a fiercer age,
when the male seized and held the female not only by
means of his arms, but also by the mouth. At any rate,
the mouth is often used by animals in the fierce struggle
of copulation. Whatever its origin, the bite in love-play,
even if it has been refined to the gentle pressure of the
teeth on the skin, may play a part, particularly in the
later stages and at the height of excitement. Even if
small teeth marks are left on a man's shoulder it must
not be considered that this is necessarily abnormal or a
sign of linking up of love with cruelty. It may be only
the outward expression of ecstasy, of a lover being carried away by an overwhelming rush of feeling.

The kisses of lovers are given elsewhere than on the
mouth. That which we love we desire to kiss, and the
loved one's hair, eyelids and body receive the caress of
the lover's lips. It has been said that certain parts of the
body are erogenous, that is to say that their stimulation
is especially likely to arouse sexual feeling. The breast
and nipples of a woman are sexual organs of high erotic
value, and are so made that they react directly to emotional stimulus, and their fondling by the loved one
gives deep satisfaction. Kisses on the breast, therefore,
may play an important part in sexual play, as well as
kisses on the body generally.

Love-play does not express itself only in kisses, but in
mutual touches and caresses. These may be carried out
by the body, but the sensitive and delicate finger tips,
next to the lips and tongue, are the best instruments for
the expression of love. The lover's touch is a light one,
which travels over the woman's body, first caressing one
part, then another, returning from time to time, and

gradually, by imperceptible stages, becoming more and more intimate. The wife does not remain passive; she returns her husband's caresses, and shows her pleasure, or if he has been inexpert, her distaste. In woman a certain diffidence or modesty may sometimes be evinced. She retreats as well as advances; an element of coquetry may play an important part during the stage of love-play. The husband should act as a courtier for his wife's favors, and she does not necessarily yield immediately to his advances. Desire is stimulated by a temporary refusal, for with many lovers the chase adds relish to the final capture. In those who have not yet become attuned to one another, a considerable amount of time should be given to these caresses, and only after a long and circuitous route should the most intimate centers be reached.

It should be emphasized that apart from the mutual joy it affords there is physiological justification for the period of love-play. All these preliminaries are necessary if the final act is to be as satisfying to the woman as to the man. They are required to lift the woman, in whom desire is roused more slowly, to the proper pitch of excitement, so that the physical changes may occur which make the female passage ready for the reception of the male organ. To neglect or shorten them is to do a physiological and emotional wrong to her.

Of all the erogenous zones in the female body, the most sensitive and stimulating is the clitoris, the tiny organ at the entrance to, and at the forepart of, the vagina. This becomes prominent in a woman who has been aroused, and so can be easily found. But the touch must be exquisitely gentle, for the clitoris is one of the most sensitive places in the whole body. This form of contact, if the wife has been properly prepared, is acutely delightful to her, and immediately increases a hundred-fold her desire. If, however, the necessary preliminaries have been cut short, or if the movements of the hand are brusque and heavy, she will shrink from the contact.

This direct stimulation of the clitoris is usually followed by a rapid mounting of desire and sexual excitement in the wife. The courting and love-play of the husband now bear fruit; she no longer retreats from him, but stirred to new levels of ardor gives as much as she receives, taking as active a part as her husband in the love-making. Her hand caresses his body as his caresses hers, thereby increasing his psychoerotic enjoyment and raising him to a still greater pitch of desire. To add to the pleasure and satisfaction of the partner and to give as much as is received becomes the mutual aim. Instinctively her whole body caresses his. Desire mounts to the zenith, and the way is quickly prepared for the initiation of the third phase of intercourse, the phase of communion. Not only is the woman now emotionally ready for it but her genital passages, relaxed and bathed in the secretions of the accessory sex glands, are properly prepared for union.

Elsewhere it will be shown that many of the dissatisfactions that are experienced on the physical side of marriage are the direct result of insufficient preparation of the wife for intercourse. Through lack of knowledge and understanding the husband attempts to penetrate his wife before she is ready for it. Because love-play has been cut short she is not only emotionally but also physiologically unready. The entrance to the vagina has to be forced, and owing to the absence of natural secretions some artificial lubricant has to be applied in order to render this possible.

Intercourse carried out in this way is both stupid and

inconsiderate; inconsiderate because it violates the wife's finer feelings, and stupid because it is bereft of the chief joy of love-making, the joy that comes from the knowledge that in satisfying one's own needs an equal satisfaction is being conferred on another. If the pleasure is not mutual love-making is shorn of most of its value; it is a one-sided indulgence, instead of the sharing of a wonderful experience.

It is perhaps unnecessary to add that throughout the whole of intercourse the greatest gentleness and sensitiveness to the partner's reactions must be maintained by the husband. Love-making does not conform to any set standard; it is infinite in its modes of expression. It is for the lover to find out, not only how he desires to express his love, but how his partner responds to his particular mode of expression. From the sublime to the ridiculous, we are told, is but a step; in love-making an equally short distance separates what may be regarded as pleasing from what is repellent. It is easy to overstep the mark; the lover must be ready to desist as well as to advance. He must be quick to perceive the slightest sign of distaste on the side of his partner. Above all he must do whatever he does with reverence, ever conscious of the fact that the instrument on which he plays is the body of the woman he loves. Sexuality may be closely allied to the tragic or to the sublime, but never to the comic. There is laughter associated with love, but it is the laughter that is the outward expression of joy, not that which springs from a sense of the ridiculous.

Many people are unaware that the physical expression of love may take many forms, sometimes being carried out in one way, sometimes in another. Experienced husbands and wives take pride in varying their approach to love, so that although the same feeling is in their hearts its manner of expression is different. Love-making must never become routine; it must never wear the drab clothes of habit. Variety, spontaneity and wonder are its attributes; even though a man and a woman have made love a hundred times before, still there must remain for them a feeling of freshness and wonder. For there is truly wonder in love, and something of the mystery that is attached to the other great realities of existence, birth and death.

The third act in the love drama is sexual communion. It begins with the insertion of the penis and ends in the climax or orgasm. In its ideal form husband and wife take an equal share in it. The passive wife deprives not only herself but her husband of full satisfaction. Husband and wife are equal partners in a rite which represents not only the union of two bodies but the fusing of two souls. As the first and second acts of a play lead up to the climax of the third act, so do all the preliminaries of intercourse serve only to lead up to the culminating glory of bodily union.

The mounting of excitement and sensation that end in the crisis of orgasm is brought about by the friction produced through an automatic succession of stroking or thrusting movements. But before these can be initiated the erect male organ must enter the prepared female passage. And here let it be noted that few husbands are capable of penetrating without the co-operation of the wife. She must guide the male organ in the right direction, and help to adjust the alignment of bodies so that this may be accomplished. Intercourse may be achieved in many different positions, but for the purpose of this description it is assumed that it is being carried out in the most usual attitude, with the wife lying on her back, her partner kneeling between. Part of his weight is supported by her and part by his own knees and elbows. Whilst the wife participates in the intercourse, her movements, as a rule, are slighter, although at times roles may be exchanged so that it is she who assumes control. This she does by bringing forward the whole pelvis and swinging it back so as to increase friction. But there is a danger if these movements are too vigorous of breaking the link, or else that overstimulation of her husband will result in a premature ejaculation. Care and co-operation are necessary if these dangers are to be avoided.

It must always be borne in mind that the woman usually requires a longer time to reach her climax than does the man. Her husband must, therefore, contrive somehow to delay his own orgasm until she is ready for hers. This he cannot do by any direct effort of will, but by reducing the sensations coming from his sex organ by occasionally stopping all friction. The understanding male lover controls not only the intensity of the sensations coming from his sexual organ but also his psychoerotic excitement by deliberately diverting his mind elsewhere. Whenever he feels that an ejaculation is imminent he should for a moment cease all movement and by every means in his power cool down his excitement until the feeling of impending orgasm passes off. Then once more he resumes movement until again it becomes necessary to stop.

One writer on the subject compares sexual intercourse with a race in which the runners start at the same moment and aim—at an equal and not too rapid pace—to attain the goal side by side. This simile is a good one, and the man, being by nature the faster runner, must, if he is not to reach the end too soon, occasionally shorten his pace or even pause in order that his partner may catch up with him. More especially must he do this when the partnership is a comparatively new one and his wife still an inexpert runner. It may take a considerable time for a woman who is not naturally highly sexed to attain erotic efficiency, and if she is left too far in the rear she will be in danger of never reaching the goal. With practice, however, she will learn to accelerate her orgasm so as to reach it at about the same time as her partner.

At the same time as he controls his own running the male must take note of what excites and aids his partner. Some women are more stimulated by complete union, whilst others only obtain an orgasm from friction against the clitoris. It is therefore necessary for the husband to find out what method of stimulation is more particularly gratifying to his wife. These discoveries are made by mutual exploration, each partner aiding the other to reach the goal of a more or less simultaneous and satisfactory orgasm.

As has previously been stated, sexual intercourse is a natural and spontaneous expression of two people's feelings for each other, and cannot, therefore, be looked upon as an activity that can be carried out in accordance with some arbitrary plan. It would, therefore, be an error to embark on an unnecessarily complicated description of the nonessential details of sexual communion. All that it is necessary to do is to state general broad principles and to draw attention to certain pitfalls into which the unwary may tumble. The rest may be left for the individual to discover by co-operation with his partner and by a process of trial and error.

Let it be repeated, love is an art, not a science. All the instructions that can be given are of the same nature as those that can be given to anyone who is about to start on the practice of any art, that is to say, they include certain general hints concerning the nature of the materials that he will use, the principles that govern their employment, and the chief difficulties that he is likely to run up against in the practice of his art. No work on music has ever taught two people to play a duet; no book on sexology has ever enabled an inexperienced husband and wife from the very beginning to start as expert lovers.

What actually takes place at the moment of the climax of the sexual act, namely the orgasm, is far better known in the case of the male than it is in that of the female. Since it is with the emotional side of intercourse that we are here chiefly concerned, attention will be paid to its psychological attributes rather than to its biological purposes.

The orgasm has been compared by several writers to the discharging of a Leyden jar. It is, of course, well known that this electrical storage apparatus is able to retain only a certain charge of electricity, and that when charged to a maximum it is liable suddenly to discharge itself when any conductor is brought into its neighborhood. What happens in the human body during sexual intercourse is somewhat similar. During the whole of sexual communion there occurs a steady mounting of what may be called "tension" in the central nervous system. Feeling and sensation rise to such heights that it is felt that any further increase would be unbearable, and just at the moment when this seems to be the case a sudden explosion occurs which results in an immediate relief of nervous tension.

When the fullest sexual experience has been attained this sudden release of nervous energy is associated with a change of consciousness, and it is for this reason that it has been said that through sex a man or a woman may experience something that is closely allied to a mystical state. At or shortly after the orgasm the sense of time may change, so that thoughts pass through the mind too fast for expression in words. Life becomes vivid, the sense of existence intensified, and ordinary feelings, the sensations and thoughts of everyday life appear poor and colorless compared with those experienced at that moment.

But such intensity of feeling cannot last, and at the end of what may seem a timeless period, but which measured by the clock is trifling, the man or woman slips back into the heavier atmosphere of everyday life. Laughter or tears, pleasure or pain seem an equally appropriate or inappropriate expression of what has happened, yet because some expression of feeling becomes essential tears or laughter follow, without either action seeming to be related to the recent experience. As one who has been carried into another world on the wings of an anesthetic laughs or cries on coming back to earth, so does a lover who has reached unaccustomed heights on the wings of love laugh or cry when the flight is over.

Although the physical accompaniments of the orgasm are less clearly understood in the case of the woman than in that of the man, it is probable that muscular contractions occur which play an important part in facilitating fertilization. In any case the psychological attributes of the climax are the same, at the lowest an intensification of voluptuous sensations, at the highest a taste of ecstasy.

The orgasm is followed by a release of all nervous tensions. Satisfied and relaxed, the lovers lie in each other's arms, their minds gently stirring with the thrill of what has so recently been experienced. As intercourse begins gradually and almost imperceptibly in the prelude, so it fades in the gentle caresses of the afterplay, the fifth and final phase of the love drama. Here, as in the initial phases of the act abruptness is to be deprecated. Let the husband avoid a sudden breaking off of the love act, or any suggestion that because his sexual needs have been satisfied he can turn his attention to other things; for just as the woman is slower in reaching the zenith of sexual communion so with her is the descent from that zenith more gradual and prolonged.

The enormous charge of energy that has suddenly been released at the moment of orgasm quite naturally leads to a feeling of fatigue. The appropriate sequel is sleep, and contented and quite satisfied the two lovers slip into unconsciousness. The duration of fatigue varies in different individuals and on different occasions. During it the sexual organs are incapable of responding to further excitation. Until restoration has taken place all psychological or physical stimulation is powerless to produce a fresh erection. But in the young and passionate restoration rapidly takes place.

It is probable that this phase of love, the afterplay, is the most neglected of all. Many males develop the habit of turning over and going to sleep immediately after the end of intercourse. By doing so they show that they have no idea of the woman's attitude to intercourse and of her need for words and caresses long after the voluptuous moments of the orgasm are over. To say the least of it, to break off thus abruptly is ungallant; but to say that and no more is to express inadequately the sense of loneliness, disappointment and frustration which may assail the wife as she lies wide awake and dissatisfied.

Surely a husband should be as assiduous in his attentions *after* his desires have been gratified as before? It must be remembered that words mean more to a woman than they do to a man, and that even though physical intercourse has proved it, she still longs to be told in words that her husband loves her and appreciates her caresses. Those words, a kiss, a tender touch, an embrace make all the difference to her. Afterplay sets the seal on sexual union. Even though the communion of bodies is over, the communion of souls still remains, and too abrupt a termination of this most intimate relationship naturally leaves the woman with a sense of affront. She has yielded everything that is in her possession to her husband, and he has, almost without a word of thanks, of appreciation, or of love, turned over and gone to sleep. The whole affair to her seems to have ended in anti-climax.

So let the crescendo of the prelude find its counterpart in the diminuendo of an epilogue—tenderly-spoken words of love, a gradually diminishing intensity of caresses and kisses, a final embrace, and then, when both partners desire it, sleep. Should sleep not be the goal, but rather a renewal of caresses and a return to sexual intimacies, it must still remain a golden rule that the tide must be allowed to run to its lowest ebb before the flow begins. Premature attempts to revive excitement and impatient efforts to excite desire are not only likely to end in failure, but may be productive of harm.

III. The Role of the Wife in Sexual Intercourse

So far in dealing with sexual intercourse, emphasis has been placed on the responsibility of the husband. It has been repeatedly pointed out that he must show every consideration for his wife, make every effort to satisfy her needs, study her reactions, and play the part of the lover and courtier, and not that of the husband with conjugal rights. Though this is so, it does not mean that the wife merely accepts and plays only a passive part in the conjugal embraces. Just as an unskillful husband may spoil intercourse for his wife, so a thoughtless wife may be responsible for sexual disharmony. It is advisable to refer here to a few points in her sexual technique that may have repercussions on the husband.

Just as there are expert male lovers who through their proficiency are able to arouse the desire of women inclined to be sexually cold, so there are women who are such mistresses of the erotic art that they can stimulate a weakly-sexed man. Such women know all the ruses by means of which a man can be stirred, and how to vary at different times their repertoire according to their partner's need. Nor is there anything that a woman need be ashamed of in acquiring this art, for does not love take even a more important place in the life of a woman than in that of a man? There is, perhaps, a particular tendency for the Anglo-Saxon wife to look with disfavor on erotic skill. At any rate English women, rightly or wrongly, are reputed in Latin countries to be cold and sexless, and to be but little interested in the physical side of love.

It is almost a pity that an inexperienced and ignorant wife cannot be sent for tuition to some member of her own sex who understands the artistry of love. She would learn a great deal. Take for example the art of disrobing. The removal of a few garments may be thought a simple matter, but it can be so done that by watching it a man can either be converted into an ardent lover or be made inclined to turn away his head embarrassed and disillusioned. Nor is it necessary to be beautiful or smartly dressed in order to stir a man's sexual desires. There is an art in wearing clothes, in adding some touch of color, in doing the hair, in a hundred small points connected with the personal appearance that are independent of income.

Personal cleanliness, an appearance of freshness, attention to such matters as attractive underclothing—all these points, small though they may appear to be, can play a part in stimulating a husband's desire. Even that much-advertised evil "body odor" can act as a deterrent to intercourse. Smell plays a large part in the sexual intercourse of animals, and although the sense of smell in a man is almost rudimentary compared with that of the animals, a pleasing or an unpleasing odor may increase or diminish, as the case may be, sexual attraction. It is, indeed, no mere accident that women from the beginning of time have made use of artificial perfumes in their toilet. The smell of lilac may bring back in a flash to a man the memory of a garden in which he walked in childhood, the odor of violets a woman he once loved, or of geranium a certain country cottage. In the same way scent that is associated with love may have a strong aphrodisiac value, and instinctively woman has always known this. That is why the mistress of the erotic arts uses it. Though man may appear to pay little attention to such trifles, they have more effect on him than some wives believe to be the case.

Behavior is as important as appearance, and more particularly her behavior during the prelude to love-making. A wrong gesture, a manifestation of indifference or irritation, an abrupt manner, a crude remark or sign of impatience may have a devastating effect on her husband's mood. So important, indeed, is a wife's behavior, that when marriage relations go wrong, it is often necessary for the expert who is called upon to deal with the situation to interview the wife and to suggest certain changes in her attitude to intercourse.

Wives who feel it is the husband's duty to make all the advances, fail to realize that there can be no true communion if the male is the only active participant.

A woman must also always remember that a husband who is lacking in confidence is a husband who is at the same time sexually weak. Should any failure on his part to complete intercourse be greeted with contempt it is quite likely that what might have been only a temporary difficulty will be converted into permanent impotence.

A man is extraordinarily sensitive to any aspersions cast on his virility, and to be humiliated in the eyes of his wife is one of the most trying experiences he can be subjected to. Mistresses are often successful where wives fail, because they are students of psychology, and particularly of sexual psychology. There is more aphrodisiacal quality in the magic touch of a woman's hand than there is in the most potent medicine. To quote a well-known authority, "Autobiographies of great men often reveal the fact that they got their inspiration from the woman who praised their efforts and stimulated them, while the haughty wife who felt herself above all things sexual could never understand the mysterious incentive which might be generated by a little erotic play."

IV. EARLY DAYS OF MARRIAGE

So far we have dealt only with the physical intercourse between two people who have already had some experience of its mysteries. We have not yet considered the earliest days of intercourse, nor the first sex act. If great emphasis has been placed on the responsibility of the husband in the technique of love-making when his wife is no longer a virgin, still greater emphasis must be placed on his responsibility during these earliest days of

physical intimacy. Let us therefore begin at the beginning.

Some degree of modesty is inevitably associated with
the sexual function. This modesty is not merely a product of civilization, an artificial atmosphere created
around a natural function. If there were no modesty,
sexuality would be considerably weakened; and where
modesty has been thrown to the winds, as has occurred
at certain times and in certain civilizations, sexual desire
has fallen. Even amongst animals a certain degree of
modesty exists. The subhuman female desires sexual relations, but shows an initial diffidence and responds to the
earlier advances of the male with an effort to escape.
These struggles on the part of the female to escape, form
indeed part of the love-play seen amongst animals. The
initial effort to escape is not only a playful allurement;
it seems to mark a definite struggle between the elemental urge to yield and an equally instinctive shyness
and dread of submitting. The final victory of desire over
dread is usually slow and difficult, and no brutal violence
must be brought into play in order to hasten it. The
maiden shows even more strongly than does the young
female animal this conflict between desire and modesty,
and every husband must realize the necessity for patience
and delicacy in the early days of marriage. Modesty must
be overcome by persuasion and not by violence.

It must be recognized, however, that in addition to
the modesty which is a natural accompaniment of her
sex, there is also a modesty that has been deliberately
and artificially cultivated in woman by man for his own
purposes. At one time women and children were brought
up in ignorance of sexuality, and the entirely innocent
and excessively modest virgin was believed to add zest to
the marriage bed. A man might himself have previously

lived a life of profligacy, but his bride was supposed to be not only modest but entirely ignorant of "the facts of life."

Fortunately, this mistaken view is no longer held, and girls are not now deliberately brought up in a state of ignorance. The vast majority of women, by the time they come to marriage, already know what are called "the facts of life," even though they have no practical experience of what sexual intercourse entails. Nevertheless and in spite of this knowledge, the innate modesty of the female still survives; and because his bride is not ignorant a man must not assume that the initiation of marriage will not entail for her a certain emotional conflict. Nor does this conflict consist merely of a dread of the pain that the consummation of the marriage may inflict upon her; it is something much deeper, something that is generally spiritual rather than physical. In any case, whether the reluctance of a bride is unconscious, subconscious or conscious, it has every claim to recognition and respect.

The chief bodily obstacle to the consummation of marriage is the hymen, the thin circle of skin at the entrance to the vagina. This varies in thickness as well as in completeness in different women, so that the obstacle it presents to consummation differs greatly in different cases. In a few exceptional instances it may be so considerable as to constitute a serious barrier to intercourse, and the hymen and vagina may have to be dilated by a doctor in order that the marriage may be consummated. These cases are, however, quite infrequent, and as a rule the hymen is readily stretched or ruptured. If all attempts to penetrate end in failure it is necessary to have recourse to dilation under an anesthetic.

Undue emphasis has been placed by the general public on the pain associated with the rupture of the hymen. Sometimes this emphasis has been so exaggerated that both parties approach the physical intimacies of marriage with dread and anxiety; the wife on account of the pain she will experience, and the husband on account of the injury he is called upon to inflict on her. Yet, if consideration, patience, gentleness and restraint are shown by the man, the consummation of marriage need not be painful.

In any case, if the bride-to-be dreads the ordeal, she may carry out before her marriage a certain amount of preliminary stretching by the fingers. She should know, however, that though digital stretching may be useful, the ideal method of dilation is not by the fingers, but by means of the organ specially fitted for that purpose, the male penis, as it slides along the vestibule and into the slight aperture that exists between the two labia. With a slight increase of pressure the membrane stretches itself, or else splits backwards, generally in two places.

The stretching or splitting may be made a very gradual process, if the couple agree to restrict their first few attempts at intercourse to this purpose. On the other hand, they may decide to complete it at once, even if the completion is associated with the infliction of pain. Should the more abrupt method of entry be decided upon, the pain is quite brief, and easily bearable by a woman with a normally thin hymen and an average nervous sensibility. If, also, the woman has the courage, instead of shrinking or giving way before the pressure, to respond by a rapid counterpressure, the hymen can be ruptured in a moment, so that the penis slips into the vagina. The loss of blood accompanying this act is as a rule only trivial, and if the bride lies quite still, with closed legs, and avoids for a time all further activity, it readily ceases.

Only in very rare cases is the bleeding sufficient to make it necessary to apply continuous pressure by means of a towel. It must be remembered, however, that after the hymen has been ruptured time must be given for the healing of the tiny wound inflicted. Intercourse must not immediately be repeated, and if necessary, a day or two must be allowed to elapse until all soreness has disappeared. While such soreness exists, special cleanliness must be observed, and some simple lotion applied, so as to keep down any possibility of inflammation. Should the attempt to consummate the marriage have failed, further efforts had better be postponed until the next day, for too prolonged or too often repeated efforts on the part of the man may bring about, not only an increased sensitiveness to pain, but a nervous reaction on the part of the bride. At all costs, fear and nervous apprehension must never become associated in her mind with physical intercourse. If it does, it may take a long time before she can become sexually adjusted.

Yet it is as easy for a husband to be too sentimental and diffident as to be too brutal. Prolonged postponement of consummation can do harm in a variety of ways. Not only may it impose an unnecessary nervous strain on both parties, but it may lead to an exaggerated idea of the difficulty of intercourse. It may be said that, if after four or five attempts to consummate marriage, intercourse still apparently remains impossible, a doctor should be consulted in order to make sure that there exists no physical obstacle requiring medical treatment.

It must be remembered that in the case of a newly-married woman, who has not yet felt the full force of sexual desire, the secretions poured out by the accessory sexual glands may be insufficient to provide good lubrication. It may well happen, therefore, that some additional lubricant is necessary in order to allow of the entry of the male organ into the vagina. Many lubricants have been suggested, ranging from the natural lubricant of the saliva to special preparations containing tragacanth sold by the chemist in tubes. Vaseline is perhaps that which is most commonly resorted to, but for those who dislike this somewhat messy material, one of the jellies is preferable.

It would also be wise for the newly-married couple to remember that the idea that the marriage should be consummated during their first night together is entirely a conventional one. Sometimes, both parties are so tired by the events of the day, and the hard work that has preceded it, that they are more inclined to sleep than for undertaking the important step of consummating their marriage. If this be the case, it would be wise for them to confine themselves to certain preliminary endearments and intimacies, and by mutual agreement to postpone complete intercourse until a future occasion.

Finally, it must be remembered that although the chief responsibility for initiating physical marriage lies with the husband, his wife must take some share in it. Intercourse, as has already been shown, is not inflicted by the male on the female, but is an activity in which both play their parts. So also in the initial phase of consummation the bride must assist her husband. No man is capable of making entry without, not only the consent, but also the co-operation of his wife. In case of physical difficulty it is sometimes helpful to place a pillow under her hips so as to bring the pelvis and the vulva into a more forward position.

An unruptured hymen is not the only physical obstacle that may make difficult the consummation of marriage. Sometimes penetration is made difficult by the muscles that surround the vagina going into a condition of spasm. Whenever the husband approaches her, however much the wife desires to receive him, these muscles contract painfully so that he cannot make an entry. The slightest touch or even the anticipation that she is to be touched starts a series of painful cramps. This condition is known as vaginismus. Occasionally it is due to local tenderness, the vagina contracting to a touch that is painful in the same way that any part of the body is withdrawn on feeling a sudden discomfort. More often than not, the reaction is not so much a physical one to pain as a psychological one. In the woman's mind the idea of intercourse is associated with some grave anxiety or fear. She is terrified of sexual intimacies, consciously or subconsciously, and because of this terror attempts to avoid it by this mechanical contraction of the muscles that guard the entrance to the vagina. Sometimes this is due to her having had an unhappy or unsatisfactory premarital experience of which the memory recurs on her marriage night.

Naturally, vaginismus, or painful spasm of the vagina, is more likely to be found in neurotic and easily frightened women brought up with a wrong attitude of sex. It has much in common with the anxiety form of impotence frequently met with in men of a similar type, and in both cases it is the fruit of wrong upbringing. It is another instance of the truth of the saying that marriage happiness or unhappiness may be determined so long ago as in childhood. Irreparable damage may result from the wrong approach of a boy or a girl to the mystery of physical love, far greater wrong than is likely to be caused from any temporary indulgence in masturbation. Yet, whilst all parents are filled with a fear that their children may masturbate, few are alive to the importance of their learning about sexuality without any anxiety being implanted at the same time.

The existence of any degree of vaginismus in a bride calls for the exercise of the greatest care and restraint on the part of the bridegroom. If he attempt to overcome the spasm by force, he will only succeed in aggravating the condition; if he desists and confines his efforts to combating the fears and anxieties of his bride he may little by little so gain her confidence that she will be able to submit to greater and greater intimacies. Usually, however, when vaginismus is well marked, medical treatment will be required in order that the marriage may be consummated.

After the bridal night, or night of consummation, comes the honeymoon, and concerning this period there is often as much misunderstanding as there is on the subject of consummation. To the bridegroom before his marriage the honeymoon sometimes appears as a season of ever-renewed embraces and intimacies, uninterrupted by the claims of everyday existence. It is to be a season of blue skies with no cloud in sight, and there will be nothing to hinder the supreme business of love. As a rule the honeymoon turns out to be quite otherwise, and there are few couples who will not afterwards have to confess that in the honeymoon sky there were clouds as well as brightness. For the honeymoon is in reality a period of apprenticeship, of learning a new art through the painful process of trial and error. It is a school as well as a holiday, a school in which the exercise of restraint and patience is as necessary as it is in the business of life. Rome was not built in a day, nor is sexual harmony attained in a week or even a month. No limit can indeed be put to the duration of this schooling, for the writer has known of married couples who have only attained complete satisfaction for each other's sexual needs after the passage of many years.

It is on the husband that the initial responsibility for the success or failure of the physical side of the marriage mainly devolves. This responsibility of the husband rests on no arbitrary decision but on the conditions imposed by Nature herself, for unless the bride has had previous sexual experiences she will approach marriage less sexually awake than her husband. Inexperienced though he may be, he is nevertheless the more advanced of two beginners, and as such must take the lead. To his bride the intimacies of the marriage bed may as yet have no meaning beyond the fact that she is giving to the man she loves what he wants and has looked forward to. It is her wedding gift to him, the greatest gift in her power to give—but apart from the pleasure of giving she herself may derive from the physical side of her marriage very little satisfaction. Her sexuality still lies dormant, waiting to be awakened by the first kiss of love, a tender possibility to be made or marred according to her husband's skill or unskillfulness. Small wonder therefore that a man who is conscious of this responsibility approaches his marriage with anxiety as well as with joy.

In the great majority of cases the woman's awakening must be gradual. Especially is this so if as a result of wrong advice or teaching she has learnt to look upon the physical side of marriage as a rather brutal tribute that must be accorded to the male animal. This was the early Victorian feminine view of marriage, and it still may persist in the minds of some women of today. Only by great gentleness on the part of the bridegroom, by courting her favors rather than assuming that they will be given, by remaining the lover as well as the lawful husband, can this wrong conception of marriage be corrected. Step by step, advancing slowly, retreating when necessary, avoiding all sudden or severe demands, he must set himself to awaken what sleeps within his wife. Especially should rest and consideration be given to the woman in the days that follow consummation, whilst the structures at the entrance to the genital passages still remain sore and tender. The exercise of restraint, the putting of her feelings and comfort before his own desires, will always be remembered by his wife. Instead of looking back on the early days of her marriage as many women unfortunately do with aversion and distaste, she will look back on them with pleasure and gratitude for the consideration shown her by her husband.

Although emphasis has been laid repeatedly on the responsibility of the bridegroom during the honeymoon, he must avoid feeling overanxious. Fear and anxiety have a paralyzing action on all sexual activity, and if the husband is unduly preoccupied with his responsibilities and too disturbed by any failure, his own sexual function may suffer. Too serious an attitude to love-making is to be as studiously avoided as is a too frivolous attitude. It was not without reason that the term love-play was applied to the preliminary intimacies that lead up to the phase of sexual communion, and no play is possible when the mind is filled with doubt and apprehension.

Let the bridegroom therefore meet his difficulties with a light heart, learning from them but not being overwhelmed by them. It were better indeed that both husband and wife should realize from the beginning that difficulties will inevitably be encountered. No marriage has ever been free from them, and the memory that by working together they have overcome them will constitute in the future yet another bond betwen husband and wife. It is well therefore that the bride and bridegroom departing for their honeymoon should realize that all newly-married couples inevitably run up against obstacles to successful union. Naturally their married friends do not tell them of their own initial difficulties, any more than they themselves will discuss such when they return from their honeymoon. These matters are kept private, and it is only the expert who hears about them in the privacy of the consulting room who realizes how common they are.

V. Variations in Sexual Intercourse

It has been pointed out that there is no standard model for the means by which a man and woman express their love for each other. Just as kisses vary, so by assuming different attitudes may the phase of sexual communion be varied. Oriental works on the art of love describe as many as a hundred methods of intercourse, in which the attitude and motions of love are different. There is, however, a disposition on the part of many married couples to feel that only certain methods of love-making are right and proper, and that others are illegitimate or degrading. If that is their opinion, then they must limit themselves to the models they have accepted. For others, on the other hand, to whom that which is mutually pleasing and satisfying is right and that which to either party seems objectionable is wrong, a greater range of variation in carrying out intercourse is permissible.

Broadly speaking, there are two main positions in intercourse; the first, in which the man and woman meet face to face; the second, in which the man faces toward the woman but the woman turns her back. All the methods of intercourse are variations of these two fundamental positions.

In the face to face position, while most of the man's weight is borne on his elbows, some rests on the woman. This may be a disadvantage if his weight is considerable or if his wife is pregnant. In such cases the position can be reversed, the wife being uppermost, or it may be varied by the wife lying quite flat with a cushion under her loins and her thighs more widely extended so that they are clasped by those of her husband. This brings the base of the penis and the clitoris together, thereby increasing stimulation but reducing the depth of penetration.

Sometimes, after childbirth, the passage has been so stretched that intimate contact is difficult to maintain in the face to face position, in such circumstances penetration at a slightly different angle will provide the necessary friction. The wife lies on her back and lifting her legs at right angles from the hips rests them on her husband's shoulders. This raises the lower spine and brings the vaginal openings upwards and forwards, enabling the penis to press against the front of the vagina. The great disadvantage of this position is that caressing is precluded by the degree of separation involved.

The sitting position is favorable to conception and is also appropriate during pregnancy. The husband is seated, the wife sits astride; there can be mutual participation and deep penetration, but again there is the disadvantage of partial bodily separation.

A natural variation of the face to face position is for husband and wife to lie side by side. At the appropriate stage, pillows having been placed to secure comfort and balance, the wife draws up the leg on which she has been lying, her position then becoming half side and half back, while the husband in a similar manner assumes a half sideways, half above attitude. Its main advantage is avoidance of weight being imposed on the woman together with care and convenience; its disadvantage is the limitation imposed on movement.

An entirely different series of attitudes is based on penetration from the back. Both partners lie on their left sides, the husband having his left arm free to caress his wife. Owing to the direction of the vagina intercourse cannot take place if an exactly parallel attitude is adopted. The wife must flex her hips and bend forward. As the husband lies at full length the two bodies diverge and the heads are further apart. Once an entrance has been made the degree of penetration can be varied by the angle maintained. This position may be of advantage when one of the partners is tired, but it is not usually quite satisfactory for the wife. The astride position already described can also be varied by the wife sitting astride her husband with her back to him.

VI. FREQUENCY OF INTERCOURSE

Medical men are often asked how often intercourse should take place, and what should be regarded as excessive and therefore injurious to health. To this question no general answer can be given. It will depend on the make-up of the individual man or woman, on their other activities of mind and body, on a dozen different factors that will vary in different cases. The golden rule is that *love-making must be spontaneous.*

First of all, it must be accepted that moderate sexual activity has a beneficial action on the mind and body of a healthy man or woman. This does not imply that the health of a person who is unable to be sexually active need in any way be impaired by chastity. Whether this is so or not depends mainly on the motive of his chastity. If a man or a woman accepts continence willingly, and diverts the energy that would otherwise be expended on sexuality into other channels—in other words, sublimates it—he or she can remain as healthy as if happily married. If, on the other hand, a man or a woman is a prey to mental conflict, or if there is a struggle between the desire to have intercourse and the fear of its consequences, then he or she is likely to be exhausted by this struggle, and cannot be regarded as being healthy. Indeed, it is from such people, tortured by desire or frightened to give way to it, that a great number of cases of nervous exhaustion are recruited. But at the present moment we are not concerned with this problem of enforced chastity, but with the bearing of sexual activity on health. We are dealing with the benefits conferred by an active sexual life in marriage, upon those who are living together and physically attracted to each other.

Regular intercourse has a beneficial effect on the body. As the muscles are improved by exercise, so are the genital organs toned up by usage. This is shown by the fact that many women who before marriage have suffered from painful or irregular menstruation, no longer suffer from this afterwards. Intercourse also invigorates and develops the physique, and tones up the body generally. Men and women who previously were too thin or too stout often acquire a more satisfactory weight after marriage. There are many people who, although they are not conscious of any mental conflict are nevertheless worried by the problem of unsatisfied sexuality, and when this has been resolved by experience there is naturally a certain relieving of nervous tension. Sexual harmony also acts like an invigorating medicine. It helps to develop all the sweetness and strength of a man's and woman's nature.

This is not only true of sexual activity in general, but of each isolated act of intercourse. A successful erotic experience leaves behind it a sense of peace and achievement, a feeling of well-being of both mind and body. Life has been enriched by it, and the lovers are left with a feeling of the joy of existence. Only when the excitement has been too prolonged, or when intercourse has been indulged in without any real desire for it, are fatigue and lassitude likely to be experienced. If this should persist for many hours, then it must be regarded as a danger signal that perhaps the limits of activity have been exceeded, and that a greater economy of intercourse is indicated.

The frequency of intercourse, therefore, must be left to the individual's own discrimination. He or she alone knows what is his or her own capacity for sexual experience, and no outside guide can be a substitute for a man's or a woman's inner feelings.

During the honeymoon the amount of intercourse indulged in may be excessive. Novelty and curiosity give to love-making an additional fillip, so that the standard of frequency is higher than it will be when these no longer act as an added source of excitement. The man must remember, however, that intercourse imposes on him a greater strain than it imposes on his wife. He must therefore beware of establishing for her a standard that he will be unable to maintain. When he returns from the honeymoon, his work will make greater demands on his strength, and what he is able to achieve on a holiday he will be unable to maintain when back in his occupation. Fortunately, nature has provided for this danger. Whereas a woman can submit to intercourse when she does not really desire it, to a man this is impossible. Unless real desire is present, and by this is meant not only desire to please his wife, but desire for his own sake, no erection can be obtained.

Each of the partners must also remember that sexual desire and capacity are determined by his or her individual endowment. Neither can give to the other more than he or she possesses. Male and female sexual potency varies according to age, circumstances, health and the erotic and psychic influences acting on that particular person. There exist men who are highly virile and also men who naturally are of low sexuality. Nor does the degree of sexual potency depend on physique; the all-round sportsman may be poorly endowed sexually compared with the less robust sedentary worker. So also the athletic woman may be comparatively cold compared with a delicate girl. Each of the two partners must, therefore, accept what is the sexual constitution of the other, each giving what is within his or her power to give.

Not only does the sexual capacity of a man or woman vary according to constitution and temperament; it varies also at different times. Sexual desire does not remain at a constant level, but rises and falls. This is particularly noticeable in the woman, and it has been shown that in the majority of women sexuality rises and falls in relation to the menstrual cycle. Usually it is at its highest just before and just after the menstrual flow, though in some cases it may reach its peak in the middle of it. In man also periodicity exists, but it is usually less well marked. As a rule two or three sexual communions take place at short intervals, to be followed by a period of abstinence; then there is again a rise of desire. The length of the cycle varies in different men.

It will therefore be for the couple to discover after the

return from the honeymoon what is the frequency of intercourse that best meets their mutual ends. If it should be proved that one is more highly sexed than the other, and that one desires more than the other can give, let them effect a compromise, accepting the restriction as an inevitable one placed on their union by nature, and not by any unwillingness on the part of either of them to give.

Rarely are husband and wife entirely balanced. If the majority of married people were to be asked whether there was anything in their marriage they would alter, one of them would usually reply that, although he or she was entirely happy, and would not wish to be married to anybody else, the marriage would have been a trifle more satisfactory if the partner had been a little more highly sexed. It is particularly necessary that the woman should realize this incapacity of a man to give more than his power permits because, as stated above, whereas she can submit more frequently to intercourse than her desires dictate, her husband is unable to do so.

Finally, it must be realized that sexuality is strongly influenced by bodily and mental health. If, for any reason, either of these is disturbed, nature like a good economist husbands all the reserves of energy, and more particularly all unnecessary outgoing in the field of sex. A man, therefore, who is worried by business troubles, or a woman who is exhausted by her housework or her children, will quite naturally experience a weakening of desire. This diminution in sexuality should be only temporary; if no demands are made by the partner, and time is given for recovery, normal sexual relations will soon be resumed. It is therefore a great mistake for a husband or wife to assume that because the other shows no desire for sexual intimacies love has left the home.

Many a wife has become a prey to the fear that her husband has lost his heart to another woman when in actual fact he is only suffering from a temporary loss of potency due to fatigue or anxiety.

On a preceding page emphasis has been laid on the need for spontaneity in love-making. Sexual intercourse is but the physical expression of an inner emotional feeling felt for each other by two people of opposite sexes. Since emotions are not subject to routine, but arise spontaneously and unexpectedly, so also sexual intercourse must be free from routine or habit. Laurence Sterne in his novel *Tristram Shandy*, draws a sketch of Tristram's father as a creature of rigidly fixed habit. So bound to a schedule was he, that, on the first Sunday evening, the monthly task of winding up the clock was invariably followed by endearments between him and his wife. This, though the fiction of a novelist, is one that has its replica in real life. To some couples, physical intercourse is a weekly or a bi-weekly routine, and because Sunday is a day of rest, the week end is set aside for connubial enjoyment.

Love tied to routine is a travesty of love. The habitual kiss given by the husband to his wife on leaving for work in the morning, or before going to sleep, may be an indication of his affection for her, but the kisses of love are more spontaneous in their origin. Suddenly, and without previous warning, a strong emotion arises, and the prelude to love begins. It is indeed only because a bed happens to be convenient for intercourse and because by bedtime the labors of the day are concluded, that love-making generally occurs at night, but intercourse need not necessarily be confined to this time. In the lives of many married people, the most happy memories are often those of intimacies that occurred at strange times and in unexpected places.

The less love-making is subject to stage management the better. One of the unfortunate attributes of many methods of birth control is that they require a certain setting of the stage for love-making. Until certain mechanical arrangements have been made, endearments must be postponed; either the wife must retire for a few moments to complete the necessary preliminaries, or else the husband, having started on the prelude and play of love-making, is forced to break off in order to make preparations for intercourse. Should he be of a nervous temperament, or easily upset, this interruption may be quite sufficient to interfere with the following phases of sexual communion. It is therefore of the utmost importance that only those methods of birth control that necessitate the minimum of prearrangement should be adopted. Indeed, many of the difficulties experienced in the early stages of marriage are directly due to the use of ill-advised methods of contraception.

VII. INTERCOURSE DURING MENSTRUATION OR PREGNANCY

The question is occasionally asked whether it is wrong for a woman to have intercourse during the time of the menstrual flow. Two main reasons prompt this question; a belief prompted by superstition, tradition, or religious doctrine that there is something sinful in intercourse at this time, and the fear lest it may carry with it some bodily risk either for the woman or her partner. For some nations a definitive answer to the question has been given by religious teaching: at such a time a woman is unclean and to touch her is defilement. Amongst peoples whose lives are regulated by superstition the same idea prevails. To them the products of the menstrual flow are

endowed with magical and harmful properties, and a
woman at such a time must be separated from her husband. The view that intercourse during menstruation
should be avoided is therefore exceedingly widely spread.

What is the answer that science would give to this
question? Probably the great majority of doctors would
reply that there is no scientific reason why, if a husband
and wife share a mutual desire to make love at that time,
they should not do so. Intercourse during menstruation
carries with it no physical risk to husband or wife. It has
been affirmed that cases of what is known as urethritis,
or inflammation of the urethra, have been due to a
man's having had intercourse with a woman before menstruation had ceased. This idea rests on no scientific
proof. It is a loose assumption; and if there were any
danger for the male it could be avoided by careful washing after the love-making has taken place. That there is
a necessity for the sexual impulse to be subjected to a
certain amount of restraint has been emphasized, but let
us be sure that good grounds exist for any rule or regulation imposed on lovers. That menstruation is not necessarily a bar to sexual intercourse is the opinion of the
majority of modern experts. So if desire arises at such a
time there is no reason why it should not be gratified.
This reassurance will be welcome to many who are only
able to resume married life for brief intervals. Such
intervals may coincide with menstruation. By adopting
normal methods of hygienic cleanliness, this need not
prevent love-making.

The problem of intercourse during pregnancy is more
complicated. The arguments that have been brought
against it are that it may cause abortion or, if pregnancy
be more advanced, premature labor, and that should
either of these accidents happen the fact that intercourse

has recently taken place increases the risk of subsequent blood poisoning. What is the truth?

Undoubtedly there have been instances of miscarriage following intercourse, but almost always these have occurred in women who already have shown a tendency to abort. Should there be any reason for believing that a risk of miscarriage exists, intercourse must be forbidden. In any case the more violent forms of intercourse must be ruled out; gentleness is always advisable. Moreover, should the pregnancy have advanced five months or more and the abdomen be considerably enlarged, a position which does not entail pressure on the uterus should preferably be adopted. Finally intercourse should be abstained from during the last four weeks of the pregnancy.

So far we have only considered the advisability or not of intercourse on physical grounds alone. But there are psychological as well as physical factors that may enter into the case. Pregnancy has, as a rule, a profound influence on a woman's intellectual and emotional life. Sometimes the temporary change in her character is such that what previously she liked she now abhors, and what before she disliked she relishes. This change may affect her attitude to sexual intercourse; although previously she may have enjoyed it, during pregnancy it may be repugnant to her. It is on the psychological attitude of the woman to physical love that the decision to continue or to abstain from intercourse during pregnancy must chiefly be based.

The well-known authority Van de Velde is of the opinion that as a rule the attitude of the woman to intercourse when she is pregnant is determined by her attitude to it beforehand. "Where previously the sexual relationship of the husband and wife was more or less

lukewarm," he says, "and the specific gratification of the
woman during intercourse only moderate or quite inadequate, then desire, if it still exists at all, vanishes quickly
and wholly as soon as the woman knows she is pregnant."
If on the other hand the wife has gained from physical
love as much satisfaction as her husband, "then as a rule
the woman's desire, in the first half of pregnancy, does
not subside in the least; on the contrary, there can be a
temporary accentuation of desire. In the second half of
pregnancy this slowly diminishes, but remains to a certain degree till the end."

It may indeed happen that during pregnancy a wife
will feel a particular need for objective signs of her husband's love. To many a woman the physical changes of
pregnancy, the loss of her figure, the temporary eclipse
of some of her charms, are particularly depressing. She
may feel that she is no longer attractive to her husband,
and that because this is so she is in danger of losing his
love. The knowledge, therefore, that whatever changes
may have taken place in her body, she still thrills and
attracts him physically brings to her great relief.

Moreover, there is another objection to any abrupt
termination of sexual intimacies during the early months
of pregnancy, namely the health and comfort of the husband. If he is healthy and sexually robust it is difficult
for him to break off sexual relations and yet continue to
be affectionate toward his wife. It is as though he were
repeatedly called upon to begin the prelude of love and
then, just as desire began to arise in him, to break off
and go away. The strain imposed on a sexually vigorous
man in playing such a role may be too hard on him.

Finally, there remains the question: how long should
abstinence be observed after the birth of the child?

The time taken for a woman to recover from childbirth differs greatly with individual women and in different races. But what really should be taken into consideration in order to mark out the duration of this time is not so much how long the woman requires to recover from the ordeal of birth, but how long the enlarged womb takes to resume its normal size. The process by which the genital organs of the delivered woman return to normality is known as "involution," and according to the authorities on the subject it takes from five to eight weeks. . . . During this period of involution the uterus and the vagina are considered to be particularly liable to infection, and therefore it is advised that intercourse should not be indulged in. Also it is held by some authorities that if sexual relations are resumed too soon bleeding may be provoked.

If, however, gentleness be observed it is not necessary for a couple to remain apart until the uterus has completely returned to its ordinary size, that is to say, for so long as about six weeks after the birth of their child. Many women return to their household duties three weeks after their confinement, and there is no reason in this case why intercourse should not be resumed then very gently and carefully, so that it becomes normal a few weeks later. It is, of course, important that a woman who has just borne a child should not again immediately conceive.

Glossary

ALGOLAGNIA: The association of sexual pleasure with pain.

ANACLITIC: From the Greek "leaning against"; the choice of a love-object may be determined by dependence on the person who originally satisfied the child's nonsexual needs; relating to dependence upon another or others.

ANAL EROTISM: Sensations experienced in the anal area; in childhood through the act of defecation.

ANESTHESIA: Loss of feeling or sensation.

ANLAGE: Hereditary predisposition; a particular genetic factor predisposing to a given trait.

ANOREXIA: Hysterical loss of appetite and loathing for food.

AUTOEROTISM: Sexual gratification through self-stimulation physically or through fantasy.

AUTONOMIC: Not under control of the central nervous system; nonvolitional.

BISEXUALITY: Containing both masculine and feminine tendencies, both constitutional and emotional.

CASTRATION: Removal of the testicles in the male, the ovaries in the female.

CASTRATION COMPLEX: Anxiety associated with unconscious fantasies of punitive mutilation of penis (male) or clitoris (female) by parental authority.

COITUS INTERRUPTUS: Termination of sexual intercourse by withdrawal so that emission takes place outside the vagina.

COITUS RESERVATUS: Sexual intercourse prolonged by control over emission; delayed orgasm or no orgasm at all.

CUNNILINGUS: Apposition of the mouth to the female genital organs. Also *Cunnilinctus.*

DETUMESCENCE: Stage of declining sexual excitement after orgasm occurs. See *Tumescence.*

DYSPAREUNIA: Painful sexual intercourse.

EJACULATIO PRAECOX: Premature ejaculation; emission before or immediately after penetration of the vagina.

ERETHISM: Sensitiveness to stimulation.

EROTOGENIC ZONES: Regions of the body habitually, or occasionally, associated with erotic excitability.

EXHIBITIONISM: The impulse to display the body, especially the genital region, with conscious or unconscious sexual motives.

FELLATIO: Apposition of the mouth to the male genital organs.

FETISHISM: Sexual attachment to some object or article; sometimes attainment of sexual gratification exclusively from nongenital parts of the body.

FRIGIDITY: Lack of sexual gratification in coitus.

GONAD: The basic reproductive organ; testicle (male), ovary (female).

HERMAPHRODITE: One with the organs and characteristics of both sexes; a rare condition more apparent than actual.

HETEROSEXUALITY: Normal sexual impulses toward persons of the opposite sex.

HOMOSEXUALITY: The existence of sexual impulses toward persons of the same sex.

HYPERESTHESIA: Extreme sensitivity to touch.

IMPOTENCE: Inability to achieve erection or perform coitus; usually a symptom of unconscious conflict.

INCEST: Sexual gratification with a member of the same family, or unconscious wish for such gratification.

INVERSION: Homosexuality.

LABILE: Referring to the lip-like folds of skin of the female genital tract.

LATENCY PERIOD: Period between the close of infantile sexual development at the age of 4-5 and the onset of puberty.

LESBIANISM: Homosexual practices between women.

LIBIDO: Term used by Freud to describe the manifestations of energy from the sexual impulse.

MASOCHISM: Sexual pleasure obtained from the experience of being hurt, physically or mentally; includes the concepts of humiliation and domination.

MENARCHE: First menstruation.

NEURASTHENIA: Condition characterized by chronic fatigue, irritability, and feelings of inadequacy.

NOSOLOGY: The branch of medical science dealing with the classification of diseases.

OEDIPUS COMPLEX: The child's early attachment to the parent of the opposite sex, accompanied by fantasies of destroying the rival parent; *Electra complex* is sometimes used to distinguish the girl's relationship to her father.

ORAL EROTISM: Sensations experienced from stimulation of the area of the mouth.

ORGASM: The terminating climax of the sex act; in men it is accompanied by the discharge of semen; in both sexes there is release from the erotic tension that builds up to the event.

PEDERASTY: Sexual union with a male by the anus; often mistakenly used for *Pedication*, any anal coitus.

PERVERSION: Deviation from normal sexual aims and objects.

PHALLIC PHASE: Stage of infantile sexual development when interest in the penis is predominant; applies to both sexes.

PREGENITAL SEXUALITY: Oral, anal infantile sexual impulses that exist before the phallic phase.

PRIMAPARA: Giving birth for the first time.

PSYCHOSEXUAL: Relating to the mental and emotional elements of sexuality.

SADISM: Sexual excitement or gratification from inflicting pain, physical or mental, on another person.

SUBLIMATION: An unconscious process in which sexual energy is transferred to nonsexual activities.

TRANSVESTISM: The impulse to assume the dress, habits, and ways of feeling of the opposite sex.

TUMESCENCE: The engorgement of the vessels of the sex organs leading to orgasm and detumescence.

URETHRAL EROTISM: Sexual excitation in the act of urination.

VAGINISMUS: Painful contraction of the walls of the vagina when coitus is attempted; usually reflects unconscious fear of intercourse.

VOYEURISM: Attainment of sexual pleasure from visual situations; e.g., a "peeping Tom."

Index

LAUREL EDITIONS

Distinguished, inexpensive

LAUREL SOCIAL STUDIES BOOKS

Women: C-110   50c
The Variety and Meaning of Their Sexual Experience
  edited by A. M. Krich, introduction by Margaret Mead.

The Anatomy of Love   LC-141   50c
  A unique collection of brilliant essays on the
  anthropology, psychology and philosophy of love,
  edited by A. M. Krich.

Freud: His Life and His Mind by Helen W. Puner LC-137   50c
  With a new foreword by Erich Fromm.

LAUREL CLASSICS

Bulfinch's Mythology   LX-111   75c
  Abridged for the student and modern reader by
  Edmund Fuller.

Plutarch: Lives of the Noble Greeks   LC-138   50c
Plutarch: Lives of the Noble Romans   LC-139   50c
  Companion volumes, selected by Edmund Fuller.